REAL-WORLD MATHEMATICS THROUGH SCIENCE

PACKAGING AND THE ENVIRONMENT

Christine V. Johnson

Nancy Cook, Project Director

Developed by Washington MESA

INNOVATIVE LEARNING PUBLICATIONS

 ADDISON-WESLEY PUBLISHING COMPANY

Menlo Park, California • Reading, Massachusetts • New York
Don Mills, Ontario • Wokingham, England • Amsterdam • Bonn
Paris • Milan • Madrid • Sydney • Singapore • Tokyo
Seoul • Taipei • Mexico City • San Juan

Washington MESA wishes to express its appreciation to the following people for their advice and assistance, without which this module could not have been completed:

Nancy Cook, Ph.D.
Washington MESA
University of Washington
Seattle, Washington

Christine V. Johnson
Washington MESA
University of Washington
Seattle, Washington

Mike Smith
Packaging Engineer
Willamette Industries
Bellevue, Washington

Kitty Gillespie
Office of Waste Reduction
Department of Ecology
Olympia, Washington

Washington MESA middle-school mathematics and science teachers in Seattle, Spokane, Tacoma, Toppenish, and Yakima, Washington

Project Editor: Katarina Stenstedt
Production/Mfg. Director: Janet Yearian
Production/Mfg. Coordinator: Leanne Collins
Design Manager: Jeff Kelly
Text Design: Michelle Taverniti
Cover Design: Dennis Teutschel
Cover Photo: © Shoji Yoshida/The Image Bank

This book is published by Innovative Learning Publications™, an imprint of the Alternative Publishing Group of Addison-Wesley Publishing Company.

This material in part is based on work supported by Grant No. MDR–8751287 from the National Science Foundation; Instructional Materials Development; 1800 G Street NW; Washington, DC 20550. The material was designed and developed by Washington MESA (Mathematics, Engineering, Science Achievement); 353 Loew Hall FH–18; University of Washington; Seattle, WA 98195. Any opinions, findings, conclusions, or recommendations expressed in this publication are those of Washington MESA and do not necessarily reflect the views of the National Science Foundation.

ISBN 0–201–86124–0
4 5 6 7 8 9 10–DR–97 96

PACKAGING AND THE ENVIRONMENT

CONTENTS

Activity 5. More Is Less   61

Family Activity. Cereal Box   73

Completed Student Sheets   79

INTRODUCTION

Packaging and the Environment is one of the middle-grades instructional modules created and field-tested by the Washington MESA (Mathematics, Engineering, Science Achievement) curriculum project. Washington MESA operates on the premise that effective classroom materials should facilitate connections between classroom and real-world mathematics and science. Staff members and teachers work with scientists, mathematicians, and engineers to outline each module. Pilot modules are tested in middle-school classrooms, then revised using feedback from the teachers.

The modules weave important mathematics themes with relevant, exciting science topics. The activities are based on current reform philosophies recommended by the National Council of Teachers of Mathematics' (NCTM's) *Curriculum and Evaluation Standards for School Mathematics* and the American Association for the Advancement of Science's *Project 2061*. Students will

◆ learn mathematics and science by doing mathematics and science. Students redesign cereal boxes and observe changes in surface area for a given volume.

◆ employ a variety of reasoning processes by using several mathematical approaches to solve similar problems.

◆ learn to express themselves mathematically and scientifically as they engage in open-ended problem solving and participate in small-group discussions.

◆ learn the appropriate use of calculators by solving real problems. Students are taught how to conceptualize and set up problems they can then solve using calculators.

◆ make connections within mathematics as well as between mathematics and science. Writing Link, History Link, and Interest Link activities are included to expand the connections to other subject areas.

◆ explore careers by simulating professional roles in the activities.
Students also study careers that use mathematics and science in the
Career Link features.

Packaging and the Environment directs middle-school students toward
active involvement in learning. Students emulate real-world work environ-
ments by collaborating in small groups and striving for group consensus.
They work with concrete materials and evaluate open-ended problems—
the combination that helps the transition from concrete to abstract thinking
crucial to the intellectual development of students at this age. To ascertain
that instruction is working, assessment is integrated into *Packaging and the
Environment* activities. Assessment and instruction goals are identical.

Family encouragement can help students succeed educationally, so a
special activity involves students' families in hands-on, collaborative work.
Students work with their parents and other family members to extend what
they have learned.

Each activity begins with an Overview summarizing what students will
be doing and how the teacher needs to prepare. This is followed by background information for the teacher's use and a Presenting the Activity
section, which describes the activity in detail and suggests discussion questions and assessment strategies. Student Sheets and Transparency Masters
are provided in blackline master form (completed Student Sheets begin on
page 79). Career Link, History Link, Writing Link, and Interest Link features
are found throughout the book.

CONCEPTUAL OVERVIEW

Packaging and the Environment addresses the following mathematics topics, science topics, and NCTM standards:

NCTM Curriculum Standards

Problem Solving
  Open-Ended
  Multiple Strategies
Communication
  Verbal and Written
Reasoning
  Logical and Spatial
  Predictions and Evaluations
Mathematical Connections
  Among Topics to
  Real-world Contexts

NCTM Teaching Standards

Worthwhile Tasks
  Real-world Contexts
The Teacher's Role
  Listening and Observing
  Orchestrating Discourse
Enhancement Tools
  Calculators
  Concrete Materials
Learning Environment
  Collaborative Work

NCTM Evaluation Standards

Alignment
  Integral to Instruction
Multiple Sources
  Oral and Written
  Individual and Group
Multiple Methods
  Instructional Planning
  Grading
Mathematical Power
  Communication
  Reasoning
  Integrating
  Generalizing

Mathematics Content Standards

Number Relationships
  Cube Roots
  Exponents
  Proportions
  Percents
Computations and Estimation
  Mental Arithmetic
  Calculators
  Numerical Estimation
  Spacial Estimation
Patterns and Functions
  Tables
  Spacial Patterns
  Functional Relationships

Algebra
  Variables
  Formulas
  Equations
Geometry
  Similar and Congruent
  Surface Area
  Volume
  Rectangular Solids
Measurement
  Metric
  Linear
  Surface Area
  Volume

Science Topics

Environmental Waste Reduction
  Waste Stream
  Conservation
  Solid Waste
  Recycling
Packaging
  Design
  Careers
  Materials
Scientific Process
  Observing
  Predicting
  Hypothesizing
  Analyzing
  Concluding

ACTIVITY OVERVIEW

Overview

Middle-school students are familiar with surface area, volume, and the shape of a rectangular solid, but they probably never thought about how these mathematical applications are inherent in something they encounter all the time—cardboard packaging.

In *Packaging and the Environment,* students work in groups to explore surface area and volume relationships while learning about aspects of a career as a packaging engineer. The activities emphasize how mathematics in packaging design addresses waste reduction—a current environmental concern.

If you know a packaging engineer or an environmentalist in the field of waste reduction, invite this person to visit the class and participate in some part of this module so students can pursue their questions and ideas further.

Activity 1: Fill and Wrap It Up

Students begin exploring surface area and volume using single-serving cereal boxes. They develop processes for calculating the volumes and surface areas of congruent rectangular solids. Then each student determines the volume of a cereal boxes brought from home. They cut open their cereal boxes along the seams in order to compute the surface area, or how many square centimeters of cardboard are used. Students are introduced to the career of a packaging engineer.

Activity 2: The Root of It All

Each student redesigns his or her cereal box to make a cubical box of equal volume. They work with formulas and solve equations to determine the dimensions for their cubical boxes. The activity reinforces the idea that different rectangular solids can have the same volume. Discussions about packaging engineering continue.

Activity 3: Extra! Extra!

After completing their cubical cereal boxes, students discover they have leftover cardboard. They realize that even though different rectangular solids can have the same volume, the solids' surface areas, which represent the amount of cardboard needed to construct them, are not necessarily equivalent. Two ways to calculate the area of the extra cardboard are presented and evaluated: first students tape their extra pieces together to form rectangles and determine their areas, and then students find the surface areas of their cubical cereal boxes and compare the results to those from their original boxes.

Activity 4: Percents and Packaging

This activity provides a relevant use of percents. Students set up proportions to determine the percent of cardboard their cubical cereal boxes save. The leftover cardboard also represents a percent of the cardboard required to construct another cubical cereal box of equal volume. They will discover in most instances this is a different percent than the percent saved. Their results illustrate how the leftover cardboard can represent at least two different percents of cardboard, depending on the comparison. They see another example of this concept in the percent of paper used in packaging compared to that dumped in the waste stream.

Activity 5—More Is Less

Students manipulate centimeter cubes to investigate what happens to the surface area and the volume of a cube when the length of each side is doubled. They develop patterns and formulate conclusions to determine the effects of doubling the dimensions of their own cubical cereal box. Their discoveries reveal that a large-size cereal box, which has a side length double that of a regular-size cereal box, would require four times as much cardboard to produce; yet it would hold eight times as much cereal. This constitutes a significant savings in packaging material and presents a manufacturing and purchasing strategy for reducing waste.

Family Activity—Cereal Box

Each family is given one sheet of 8.5" × 11" cardstock paper to design and construct a cereal box they think will hold the most cereal possible. In the preceding activities the volume between the original cereal box and its resulting cubical cereal box remains constant, and the surface area varies based on the shape of the box. For the family activity the reverse is true. The available surface area is a constant 93.5 square inches, and the volume becomes the variable affected by the design of the container.

MATERIALS LIST

The following is a consolidated list of materials needed in *Packaging and the Environment*. A list of materials is included in the Overview for each activity.

Activity	Materials
Fill and Wrap It Up	*For each student:* ◆ Student Sheets 1.1–1.3 ◆ Cereal box (brought from home) ◆ Scissors, centimeter ruler, and scientific calculator *For each group of students:* ◆ 1 or 2 single-serving cereal boxes ◆ Clear tape and masking tape ◆ A sheet of centimeter graph paper ◆ 300 one-centimeter cubes
The Root of It All	*For each student:* ◆ Student Sheet 2.1 ◆ Cereal box from Activity 1 ◆ Scissors, centimeter ruler, and scientific calculator ◆ Student Sheet 1.1 (for reference) *For each group of students:* ◆ Masking tape *For the teacher:* ◆ A demonstration cube ◆ Transparency of Student Sheet 2.1 ◆ Transparency pen
Extra! Extra!	*For each student:* ◆ Student Sheets 3.1 and 3.2 ◆ Cubical cereal box ◆ Leftover cardboard ◆ Scissors, centimeter ruler, and scientific calculator

Activity	Materials
	For each group of students:
	◆ 100 unit cubes and masking tape
	For the teacher:
	◆ Two identical cereal boxes
	◆ Transparency of Student Sheet 3.1
	◆ Transparency pen
Percents and Packaging	*For each student:*
	◆ Student Sheets 4.1–4.4 and 3.2 (for reference)
	◆ Scientific calculator
	For the teacher:
	◆ Demonstration cereal boxes from Activity 3
	◆ Rectangle formed by taping together leftover cardboard pieces
	◆ Transparency Masters 4.5–4.7
	◆ Transparency pen
More Is Less	*For each student:*
	◆ Student Sheets 5.1 and 5.2
	◆ Scientific calculator
	◆ Student Sheets 1.3 and 2.1 (for reference)
	For each group of students:
	◆ 100 unit cubes
	For the teacher:
	◆ Demonstration cereal boxes from Activity 3
	◆ 7 additional student-made cubical cereal boxes of the same dimensions and a marker or tape
	◆ Enough cardboard to construct a cubical box double the dimensions of your demonstration cubical box
Family Activity	*For each student:*
	◆ Family Activity Sheet 1
	◆ One 8.5" × 11" sheet of cardstock
	For each family group:
	◆ 8.5" × 11" practice paper
	◆ Scientific calculator
	◆ Scissors, tape, and centimeter ruler
	For the teacher:
	◆ A full box of cereal
	◆ 4-cup graduated transparent measuring cup

RESOURCES LIST

This list of resources was compiled by teachers, scientists, and professionals who participated in developing *Packaging and the Environment*. It is intended for teachers who would like to pursue the topic further with their classes, with small groups of students who are particularly interested in the topic, with individual students who desire further investigation, or for their own professional development.

1. *Packaging for the Environment*
   Stilwell, Canty, Kopf, Montrone
   Arthur D. Little, Inc., 1991

2. *Action Plan of the Packaging Task Force*
   Office of Waste Reduction
   Department of Ecology
   Mail Stop PV–11
   Olympia, WA 98504–8711
   (206) 438–7771

3. *50 Simple Things You Can Do to Save the Earth*
   The Earth Works Group
   Earthworks Press
   Berkeley, CA 1989

4. "Stars, Fans Force Industry to Sing New Tune on CD Packaging"
   Paul Underhill, *Audubon Activist*
   October 1991, page 3

5. Institute of Packaging Professionals
   481 Carlisle Drive
   Herndon, VA 22070
   (804) 318–8970

6. Michigan State University
   School of Packaging
   East Lansing, MI 48824–1223
   (Michigan State grants both a Bachelor of Science and Master of Science degree in packaging.)

7. Willamette Industries
   1899 120th Avenue NE
   Bellevue, WA 98005
   (206) 455–1111

8. Office of Waste Reduction
   Mail Stop PV–11
   Olympia, WA 98504
   (206) 438-7771

FILL AND
WRAP IT UP

Overview

Students work with cereal boxes as a model of a rectangular solid. Each group fills a single-serving cereal box with centimeter cubes and creates a wrapping-paper network for it using centimeter graph paper. They develop methods for determining the volume and surface area of a rectangular solid. They measure and record the dimensions of a cereal box brought from home and determine its volume. They cut open this box to form a flat network and calculate the surface area. The activity introduces the career of a packaging engineer.

Purpose. Students visualize and understand surface area and volume, differentiate between them, and understand that surface area is measured in square units and volume in cubic units. They also think about how cereal boxes are designed.

Time. One to two 45-minute periods.

Materials. *For each student:*

◆ Student Sheets 1.1–1.3

◆ Cereal box (brought from home)

◆ Scissors, centimeter ruler, and scientific calculator

For each group of students:

◆ 1 or 2 single-serving cereal boxes

◆ Clear tape and masking tape

◆ A sheet of centimeter graph paper

◆ 300 one-centimeter cubes

Getting Ready

1. At least a week in advance, ask each student to bring an empty cereal box to class (be sure his or her name is on the box).

2. Determine a storage place in the classroom for the cereal boxes.

3. Purchase and prepare single-serving cereal boxes.

4. Duplicate Student Sheets 1.1–1.3.

5. Locate scissors, centimeter rulers, scientific calculators, centimeter graph paper, masking tape, clear tape, and centimeter cubes.

Background Information

Cereal boxes are designed by packaging engineers. The engineers determine the ideal shape and substance for a container based on what it will hold and how it will be used. During the design process they make several sample boxes, fill them with the product, and test them for strength, durability, and suitability. Criteria they consider before selecting the final container include environmental considerations, customer preference, efficiency, and cost-effectiveness.

This activity distinguishes linear measurements on a rectangular solid, its surface area, and its volume. Prepare the single-serving cereal boxes for each group in the class by cutting open one of the large faces along three of its edges and removing the inner bag of cereal. Opening the largest face will provide easier access for accurately filling the box with centimeter cubes. Two single-serving cereal boxes for each small group ensures every student is involved and able to benefit from the experience. Boxes can be prepared by students during one class and reused with subsequent groups.

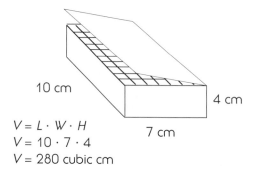

$$V = L \cdot W \cdot H$$
$$V = 10 \cdot 7 \cdot 4$$
$$V = 280 \text{ cubic cm}$$

These boxes provide a concrete introduction to volume and surface area. They are all congruent and conform to metric measurements, unlike the variety of cereal boxes from which students will be collecting data throughout this module. Working in groups on Student Sheet 1.1, students will discover a variety of ways to arrive at a process for determining the total number of centimeter cubes necessary to fill a single-serving cereal box. Some students may see patterns in the layers of cubes and will not need to fill the box to determine its volume.

On Student Sheet 1.2, students will use centimeter graph paper to produce a wrapping-paper network that represents the surface area. The interior and exterior measurements of the single-serving cereal box are slightly different due to the cardboard's thickness. Though this phenomena is true for all containers, the activities in this module do not differentiate between the interior and exterior dimensions since the differences are so small. As students trace the rectangular faces of the single-serving cereal box, they will notice this slight increase in the outside measurements. Suggest that they estimate the rectangles' dimensions to the nearest whole centimeter so the measurements conform to the inside dimensions already established.

Students can assemble the rectangles in several different ways to form a wrapping-paper network that corresponds to the faces of the single-serving cereal box. Two possible networks are displayed below.

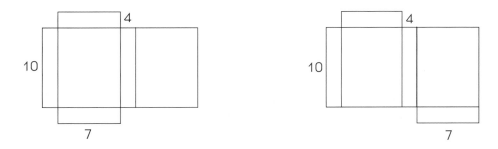

Students determine the surface area of their boxes by calculating the area of the rectangles from their paper network. They record this information in the table on Student Sheet 1.2. Look at Completed Student Sheet 1.2 (page 81) to see this table filled in.

The cereal boxes brought from home represent a rectangular solid with three sets of congruent rectangular faces. Before beginning Student Sheet 1.3, students should cut off and discard any loose flaps or overlapping parts on the top and bottom of their cereal boxes. They should ignore any excess cardboard used for seaming. They should also tear off half the top, insert the tab into the other half of the top, and tape the top pieces together. The top rectangle will then be equivalent to the bottom rectangle.

On Student Sheet 1.3, students measure the dimensions of the cereal box they brought from home and calculate its volume. They cut open the cereal box to form a flat network in order to determine the surface area. When completing Student Sheet 1.3, several students might remeasure the dimensions of each rectangle on their cereal box network. Eventually they will realize the measurements are consistent with the length, width, and height they already recorded for their cereal box when they calculated its volume. At this point students may begin to recognize a connection between the measurements used to determine surface area and volume.

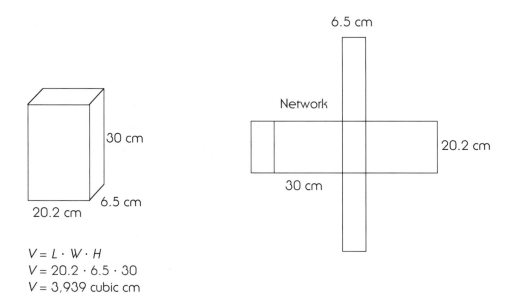

$$V = L \cdot W \cdot H$$
$$V = 20.2 \cdot 6.5 \cdot 30$$
$$V = 3{,}939 \text{ cubic cm}$$

| Rectangle | Dimensions | | Area |
	Length	Width	
Top	20.2	6.5	131.3 square cm
Bottom	20.2	6.5	131.3 square cm
Front	30.0	20.2	606.0 square cm
Back	30.0	20.2	606.0 square cm
Left Side	30.0	6.5	195.0 square cm
Right Side	30.0	6.5	195.0 square cm
Total Surface Area			1,864.6 square cm

The students will be able to measure the lengths, widths, and heights of their cereal boxes to tenths of centimeters. The error associated with these measurements is 0.05 cm. How is the error of area (the product of two linear measurements) determined? We know that error tends to compound, so it does not make sense that the result of multiplying two numbers would be more accurate than the initial numbers. In mathematics, however, we tend to ignore this problem altogether and report the area as significant to two decimal places, or to hundredths, but this is not what a scientist would do. Scientists follow a general procedure that involves the following steps:

1. Determine the error in the linear measurement. In our example, the linear dimensions of the cereal box are 6.5 cm, 20.2 cm, and 30.0 cm. The

implied error is 0.05 cm in each of these measurements. The dimensions of this cereal box are 6.5 ± 0.05 cm $\cdot$ 20.2 ± 0.05 cm $\cdot$ 30.0 ± 0.05 cm.

2. Determine the error in the calculation for area. The surface area for one face of the box would be

$$20.2 \cdot 30.0 = 606.0 \text{ cm}^2$$

The error in this calculation is determined by calculating the difference between the area derived when using the maximum values for these two measurements and the area derived then using the minimum values of these two measurements. For example:

$(20.2 + 0.05) \cdot (30.0 + 0.05) - (20.2 - 0.05) \cdot (30.0 - 0.05)$

$= (20.25 \cdot 30.05) - (20.15 \cdot 29.95)$

$= 608.5125 - 603.4925$

$= 5.02$

This can be represented in graphic form.

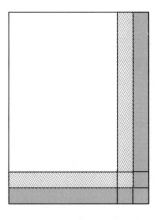

The unshaded area represents the surface area as calculated using the minimum measurements.

The entire area represents the surface area as calculated using the maximum measurements.

The shaded area represents the actual error in area due to the error in the linear measurements.

3. Determine the significant figures used to report the results. A rule of thumb used in science states that you report one more significant figure beyond the most significant figure in the error. Since the most significant figure in the error is in the ones place (5), the area should be reported to the tenths place, which is one more significant figure beyond the ones place. The area for this face would be reported as 606.0 cm^2. The area for the other faces would also be reported to the tenths place, 131.3 cm^2 and 195.0 cm^2.

The same process would be used to determine the significant figures reported in the calculation of the volume.

4. Calculate the volume as follows:

$$6.5 \text{ cm} \cdot 20.2 \text{ cm} \cdot 30.0 \text{ cm} = 3939 \text{ cm}^3$$

5. Determine the error in the calculation:

(6.5 ± 0.05) cm $\cdot$ (20.2 ± 0.05) cm $\cdot$ (30.0 ± 0.05) cm = $(3939 \pm ?)$ cm^3

$(6.5 + 0.05) \cdot (20.2 + 0.05) \cdot (30.0 + 0.05) - (6.5 - 0.05) \cdot (20.2 - 0.05) \cdot (30.0 - 0.05)$

$= (6.55) \cdot (20.25) \cdot (30.05) - (6.45) \cdot (20.15) \cdot (29.95)$

$= 3985.76 - 3892.53$

$= 93.23$

Since the most significant figure in the error is in the tens place (9), the rule of thumb says the volume should be rounded to the ones place, which is one more significant figure beyond the tens place.

The calculations throughout *Packaging and the Environment* reflect this rule of thumb. The calculations of area are rounded to tenths and the calculations of volume are rounded to whole numbers.

Talk with the science teachers in your school and decide whether you want to enter into a full discussion of error and significant figures in measurement, or if you want to give a brief overview of what scientists do, emphasizing that error accumulates and the calculations for area and volume are only as accurate as the original linear measurements. Explain that in a situation where the linear measurements are recorded in tenths, a scientist would record the calculations for area in tenths and the calculations for volume in whole numbers. The main point is that the calculations for area and volume should not be reported with more significant figures than the original linear measurements.

Presenting the Activity

Describe this Box. Divide your students into small, cooperative groups.

Hold up a single-serving cereal box and ask the class to describe it. List their responses on the chalkboard or overhead until they have determined that it is a three-dimensional rectangular solid. Now ask the following:

◆ Does the single-serving cereal box hold the same amount of cereal as the boxes you brought to class?

◆ How do you know?

◆ How much cereal does the single-serving cereal box hold?

Suggest that they use centimeter cubes as one way to measure how much cereal the single-serving cereal box holds. The total number of cubes that fit in a box represents its volume. Volume measures the space inside a three-dimensional figure, and it is measured in cubic units.

Fill It Up. Hand out Student Sheet 1.1 to each student and about three hundred centimeter cubes to each group. Suggest that students work together in their groups to answer the problems on the sheet.

When they are finished, look at their varied responses to problem 9 where they write an equation to describe a relationship between the dimensions of a cereal box and its volume. List only their formulas, which may include $\frac{V}{H} = L \times W$, $\frac{V}{L \times W} = H$, and $V = L \times W \times H$. To ensure that all students understand the relation between volume and the linear dimensions length, width, and height, ask them to discuss in their groups how they would determine the volume of the box if they knew its dimensions. This is the reverse process of what they just did. They first determined the volume and then the dimensions. Emphasize that volume is measured in cubic units.

Wrap It Up. Ask students how much cardboard they think they would need to make a single-serving cereal box. List responses on the chalkboard or overhead. Explain that the amount of cardboard needed to construct a box is referred to as its surface area. Remind students that the cereal box has six faces.

Explain that they can determine the surface area, or amount of cardboard, by using centimeter graph paper to build a wrapping-paper network for the single-serving cereal box.

Point out that students are to ignore the overlapping flaps and seams in their boxes. Although packaging engineers must include this extra cardboard in their surface area calculations, the amount is insignificant and students can ignore it for this activity.

Distribute Student Sheet 1.2 and encourage students to work together. Give each group a sheet of graph paper. When groups have completed their networks, hold up several different networks they have constructed and ask the following:

◆ Is it possible to have more than one network?

◆ What do the different networks have in common?

If necessary, point out that each network contains three sets of congruent rectangles. The box has six faces: top, bottom, front, back, left side, and right side. The network has six rectangles.

With the class or in small groups, establish that the formula for calculating the area of any rectangle is $A = L \times W$. Determine and reinforce a process for finding the surface area of the single-serving cereal box. Stress the fact that surface area is measured in square units because you are determining the total number of unit squares in the two-dimensional network. Emphasize that surface area indicates how much cardboard is needed to make the cereal box. Develop the idea that a flat, two-dimensional network of rectangles is carefully laid out and folded up to form the three-dimensional box.

Discuss the careers of packaging engineers using information provided in the Background Information and the Career Link titled "Packaging Engineers."

Box Basics. Distribute Student Sheet 1.3. Ask students to cut off and discard the inside flaps and tape the top opening together. Now they have a model of a rectangular solid. They should measure their cereal box with a centimeter ruler and then calculate its volume. Discuss error in measurements.

Students should cut open their cereal box along the seams to form a flat network. Emphasize that the network needs to be in one piece, but there is more than one possible network for any box. If students accidentally cut off a piece, have them tape it back on.

At the end of the class period have students leave their labeled cereal box networks in the classroom in preparation for Activity 2, where they redesign their cereal boxes.

Discussion Questions

1. Describe situations where you might use surface area or volume measurements.

2. Describe two ways for finding the volume of a rectangular solid.

3. Who designs cereal boxes, and why are they tall, rectangular solids?

4. How many different networks are possible for a cereal box?

Assessment Strategies

1. Explain why you were able to use centimeter cubes to determine the dimensions of the single-serving cereal box.

2. Suppose the network for the cereal box you brought from home is cut out from a single rectangular sheet of cardboard.

   a. What are the smallest dimensions that a sheet of cardboard could have?

   b. How much cardboard will be wasted in making the box?

3. How much cardboard is used in making the flaps overlap?

4. If the volume of a rectangular solid is 128 cubic centimeters, and the area of its base is 16 square centimeters, can you determine its height? Explain.

5. A cereal box's dimensions are 24 cm, 16 cm, and 5 cm. Find the area of the largest face.

Packaging Engineers

Do you like to work with objects? Are you creative and detailed? Are you good in mathematics, but also artistic? Then you should consider a career in packaging engineering. Packaging engineers determine the ideal shape and substance for a container based on what it will hold and how it will be used. Cereal boxes, ketchup bottles, and the package your pencil came in were designed by packaging engineers.

As a packaging engineer you would use paper, plastic, metals, or glass to make containers. You would design a package that would protect the product but also be easy for the consumer to use. For example, you might find ways to make detergent easier to pour, bottles easier to carry, and lunch meat easier to open and reseal.

Also, you would work with artists to design packages that sell. Your package may need to stand out on a store shelf stuffed with competitors' products. After making several sample containers, you would fill them and test them for strength, suitability, and cost.

At the Kellogg® Corporation in Battle Creek, Michigan, fifteen to twenty packaging engineers design cereal boxes such as the ones you will be working with. In a typical day they may design new packages that cost less but have better quality. They may coordinate packaging equipment designers, material suppliers, engineers, and management to help get the package from design to finish in a smooth process. They may also develop new machinery to make better packages.

As you can see, a packaging engineer has a lot of responsibilities. You would be a leader, a team member, an artist, a problem solver, and an engineer all in one. To get your bachelor of science degree you would take courses such as mathematics, physics, art, communications, computer sciences, economics, and packaging systems. Several colleges offer degrees in packaging engineering including Rutgers University, Rochester Institute of Technology, Michigan State, and San Jose State. But other colleges will allow you to design your own degree.

Fill It Up

1. Fill the single-serving cereal box with centimeter cubes to find the maximum number of cubes it can hold.

2. Based on the total number of cubes the single-serving cereal box holds, the volume of this rectangular solid is _____.

3. Volume is measured in what kind of units? _____

4. Explain your process for determining the number of cubes needed to fill the cereal box.

5. How many cubes are in one layer? _____

6. How many layers of these cubes fit in the single-serving cereal box?

   _____

7. What is the height of your box in centimeters? _____

8. Use the cubes to determine the other dimensions in centimeters of the single-serving cereal box.

   Length _____Width _____

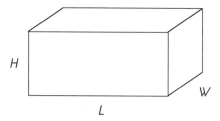

9. Write an equation to describe a relation between the length (*L*), width (*W*), and height (*H*) of a cereal box and its volume (*V*).

10. If you are given the dimensions of a rectangular box, how would you

calculate the total number of cubes it can hold? _____

Wrap It Up

1. Trace each rectangular face of the single-serving cereal box onto a sheet of centimeter graph paper. This approximately equals the surface area. Outline the dimensions to the nearest centimeter.

2. Label the pieces on the graph paper to show a top, bottom, front, back, left side, and right side of the single-serving cereal box.

3. Cut out each rectangle. Using clear tape, tape them together to form a flat network that will cover each face when it is wrapped around the single-serving cereal box.

4. Sketch your wrapping-paper network below.

5. Determine the area of each rectangle on the network. Fill in the table below.

Rectangle	Number of Squares	Dimensions (in cm) Length	Width	Area
Top				
Bottom				
Front				
Back				
Left Side				
Right Side				
Total Surface Area				

6. Area is measured in what kind of units? _____

7. If you are given the dimensions of a cereal box, how would you calculate its surface area?

8. What is the relationship between the wrapping-paper network and the amount of cardboard used to make the single-serving cereal box?

Box Basics

1. Using a centimeter ruler, measure and record the dimensions of your own cereal box to the nearest tenth of a centimeter.

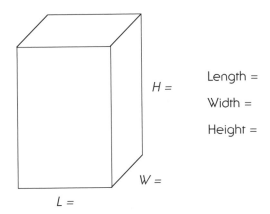

Length =

Width =

Height =

2. Calculate the volume of your cereal box using the formula for the volume of a rectangular solid.

3. Volume is measured in _____ units.

4. How many centimeter cubes will fill your cereal box?

5. Cut open your cereal box along the seams to form a flat network. If you accidentally cut a section off, tape it back on. In the space provided, draw a picture of your network. Label the dimensions.

6. Complete the table to determine the surface area of your cereal box.

Rectangle	Number of Squares	Dimensions (in cm) Length	Width	Area
Top				
Bottom				
Front				
Back				
Left Side				
Right Side				
Total Surface Area				

7. Surface area is measured in _____ units.

ACTIVITY 2

THE ROOT OF IT ALL

Overview

Each student redesigns his or her cereal box to make a cubical box of equal volume. They discuss aspects involved in determining the packaging design for products and receive more information on packaging engineering.

Purpose. Students understand that different shapes of rectangular solids can have the same volume as they learn about cube roots. They apply their work to a real-world scenario and become more familiar with the packaging industry.

Time. One to two 45-minute periods.

Materials. *For each student:*

◆ Student Sheet 2.1

◆ Cereal box from Activity 1

◆ Scissors, centimeter ruler, and scientific calculator

◆ Student Sheet 1.1 (for reference)

For each group of students:

◆ Masking tape

For the teacher:

◆ A demonstration cube

◆ Transparency of Student Sheet 2.1

◆ Transparency pen

Getting Ready

1. Locate a unit cube for the demonstration model.
2. Duplicate Student Sheet 2.1.
3. Make a transparency of Student Sheet 2.1.
4. Locate scissors, centimeter rulers, scientific calculators, masking tape, and a transparency pen.

Background Information

This activity reinforces the concept that rectangular solids with different dimensions can have the same volume. Class discussion focuses on why one style of box might be preferred over another, considering they both hold the same amount of cereal.

Through the process of designing a cubical cereal box of equal volume to their cereal box brought from home, students are introduced to cube roots. This module does not intend for students to master cube root procedures. It simply introduces a relevant application of the cube root operation. Students will need to have access to a scientific calculator to help them understand this concept.

Because the length, width, and height of a cube are equivalent, the dimension of each edge of a general cube may be referred to as E units, where E denotes the length of an edge. Therefore the volume of any cube could be stated as $V = E \times E \times E$, which is derived from the formula for the volume of a rectangular solid.

If the volume of a rectangular solid is: $V = L \times W \times H$

Substitute E for the length of an edge of a general cube: $V = E \times E \times E$

Then, the derived formula for the volume of a cube is: $V = E^3$

Cubing a number and taking the cube root of a number are opposite operations. Therefore to algebraically solve for E in the equation $V = E^3$, find the cube root of both sides of the equation. For example, here is the algebraic process to solve for E if the volume of a cube is 64 cubic centimeters.

If $\qquad V = E^3$

Then $\qquad 64 = E^3$

and $\qquad \sqrt[3]{64} = \sqrt[3]{E^3}$

Therefore $\qquad 4 = E$

The sample cereal box presented in Activity 1 with a volume of 3,939 cubic centimeters is used here to illustrate the procedure students will follow on Student Sheet 2.1 to determine the value of E for their particular cubical cereal box.

A special formula for the volume of a cube with dimension E is: $\qquad\qquad V = E^3$

Substitute the volume of your cereal box for V into the special formula: $\qquad\qquad 3,939 = E^3$

Use a scientific calculator to determine
E by finding the cube root of both sides
of the special formula.

$$\sqrt[3]{3939} = \sqrt[3]{E^3}$$
$$15.7929 = E$$

Round the display to the nearest tenth of
a centimeter.

$$15.8 \text{ cm} = E$$

After determining the length for each side of their cubical cereal box, there are several approaches students could use to construct their boxes. A few will cut out individual squares and tape them together; others will lay out their squares on the existing network before cutting. They may or may not try to keep as many faces hinged together as possible. Consider all methods resulting in an accurate cube approximately equivalent in volume to their original cereal box valid.

There comes a point in the process of cutting square faces out of their original network for their cubical cereal box where students realize not all of the squares can be cut out in one piece. They will discover at least two of the six square faces need to be pieced together.

It is imperative students keep every bit of their leftover cardboard, no matter how incidental some of the scraps may seem. They will use these leftover pieces in Activities 3 and 4 to determine how much cardboard a cubical cereal box actually saves.

Presenting the Activity

The Root of It All. Divide your students into small, cooperative groups. Hold up a demonstration cube and conduct a class discussion on the aspects of a cube. Ask students to describe it in detail. Record their observations on the board or overhead, recognizing a cube consists of six equivalent square faces where $L = W = H$.

Suppose a certain cube is 6 cm long. Ask students to decide in their groups the value of the cube's width and height. When they have determined that the width and height are also 6 cm, draw a cube on the chalkboard or overhead and label the dimensions.

Ask students to work in their groups to determine the volume of this cube. As they finish, see if they can pose an alternate way to calculate the volume of a rectangular solid when all three dimensions are equivalent. Point out how 6 cm $\times$ 6 cm $\times$ 6 cm = $(6 \text{ cm})^3$. Have students experiment using the y^x or x^y key on a scientific calculator. Let them start with an equation they know, such as $2^3 = 8$, to explore how the calculator keys work. Then have them compute 6^3.

When they recognize 6^3 is equivalent to $6 \times 6 \times 6$, ask them to propose a general formula for determining the volume of a cube with edge length E. As they determine that $V = E \times E \times E$, simplify the right side of the equation with them to develop a special formula for the volume of a cube: $V = E^3$.

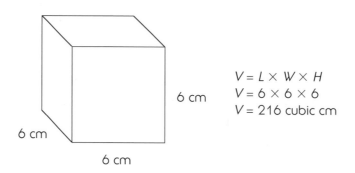

$V = L \times W \times H$
$V = 6 \times 6 \times 6$
$V = 216$ cubic cm

Roots. Ask students if they can find the length E of the edge of a cube with a volume of 64 cubic centimeters. Since $V = E^3$, by substitution, $64 = E^3$. Discuss how students might solve this problem, including trial and error and applying algebraic procedures. Once they have concluded that $E = 4$ cm, they should use their calculators and the y^x or x^y key sequence to verify that $64 = 4^3$.

Point out that cubing E and taking the cube root of E^3 are opposite operations. Explain that in order to algebraically determine E when $64 = E^3$, students actually find the cube root of both sides of the equation.

Demonstrate the algebraic procedures involved in finding the length of the edge of a cube with a volume of 64 cubic units. Review the process for determining the cube root of a number on scientific calculators.

Cubical Cereal Boxes. Explain to the class that they are going to redesign their original cereal boxes to build cubical boxes of equal volume. To do this, each student will need to calculate the value of E for his or her cereal box.

Select the actual volume of a particular student's cereal box and have students work within their groups to determine the length E, one edge of each square face of the student's proposed cubical cereal box. Suggest that they round the calculator display to the nearest tenth of a centimeter. With class input, display the process and solution on a transparency of Student Sheet 2.1 for clarification.

Distribute Student Sheet 2.1. Remind students to refer to Student Sheet 1.1 for the volume of their original cereal box. This is the volume they will use to determine *E*.

After completing Student Sheet 2.1, students should begin building a cubical cereal box. Warn students to *not throw away any cardboard scraps whatsoever*, because they will need them later. They should also be sure to keep their scraps, or leftover cardboard, separate from other classmates' leftover cardboard.

In the Real World. While students work on their cubes (or after they have finished), present this scenario: You are a packaging engineer for a new cereal company. This cubical cereal box is a new idea you thought of for packaging cereal. Now ask the following:

◆ How will your new cube affect the function of the cereal box?

◆ Who should you consult before presenting your idea to the president? (What about the machine designers who make the boxes?)

◆ How could artists design this new cereal box?

◆ What problems might your new box have?

Read and discuss the History Link "The Packaging Industry."

At the end of class, have each student carefully collect his or her cubical cereal box along with every remaining piece of cardboard and bundle them together with masking tape (or place the remaining pieces in a manila envelope and tape it to the box). Appropriately label the boxes and store them in the classroom.

Discussion Questions

1. How much cereal will each of the cubical cereal boxes hold in comparison to the original cereal boxes?

2. Why don't companies make cubical cereal boxes?

3. Does your cubical cereal box look just like all the other cubical boxes in your group? in the class? Explain.

4. Is each face on your cubical cereal box a single piece of cardboard?

5. Did you use all of your available cardboard to build your cubical cereal box?

Assessment Strategies

1. Give two possible sets of whole-number dimensions for a rectangular solid that has a volume of 512 cubic centimeters.

2. With your group, decide what determines the number of pieced together faces someone might have on their cubical cereal box. Is there a minimum number of pieced together faces someone might have on their cubical box? Why?

3. Calculate the dimensions for a cubical cereal box equivalent in volume to a single-serving cereal box.

The Packaging Industry

Imagine wrapping your cheese in animal skins, carrying your milk home in clay pots, and pouring your cereal from a woven basket. Skins, pots, cloth, and baskets were the packages of long ago. But walk into a grocery store today and you will find millions of packages made from paper, metals, plastics, glass, and even some new materials that did not exist a few years ago.

The packaging industry is on an obstacle-course race. It must keep up with technology—new computers and new machines to make packages. At the same time, it must overcome obstacles such as quality controls, safety of the packaging, and environmental concerns about waste. If the packages are to be sold in stores, the industry must also keep ahead of the rapidly changing tastes of the buyers.

This is why the industry needs many packaging engineers. As more and more products are manufactured, packaging engineers will become more in demand. Engineers can now design packages in three-dimensions on computer screens. The computer can quickly change the package's size, shape, label, color, or whatever. Packaging engineers can experiment without having to make an actual sample of the package, which saves time and money.

A push for packaging reform is sweeping the country. The industry is trying to find new ways to save material, reduce waste, encourage recycling, and limit packaging that could be dangerous for the environment (such as plastics).

Packaging engineers must balance all of these factors to keep the company in the race. They balance cost, environmental concerns, and the consumer's needs. For example, many people want food packaged in single-serving containers. The engineers must balance this need with the need to reduce material and waste by making big packages.

Although you may never have to eat cheese out of an animal skin, cheese packaging, like other packaging, will change as industry and consumers strive for better packages with less waste.

The Root of It All

You are going to redesign your cereal box to make a cube that will hold the same amount of cereal.

1. The volume of your cereal box is _____.

2. What is a cube?

3. What will be the volume of your new cubical cereal box? _____.

4. The formula for the volume of a rectangular solid is _____.

5. A special formula for the volume of a cube with dimension E is

   _____.

6. Substitute the volume of your cereal box into the special formula for V.

7. Use a scientific calculator to determine E by finding the cube root of both sides of the special formula.

   $$\sqrt[3]{} \;=\; \sqrt[3]{}$$

8. Round the display to the nearest tenth of a centimeter.

   $E =$ _____

9. What does E tell you?

10. Think about the process you will use to build your cube. Build it.

ACTIVITY 3

EXTRA! EXTRA!

Overview

Students begin to understand that even though different rectangular solids can have the same volume, their surface areas, which represent the amount of cardboard needed to construct them, are not necessarily equivalent. They construct one or more rectangles with their leftover cardboard and calculate the area. They also compare the surface area of their cubical cereal box to that of their original box.

Purpose. Students realize there are several ways to calculate the area of the leftover cardboard to find how much the cubical box saves. They learn about the roles of industry and the consumer in reducing waste.

Time. One to two 45-minute periods.

Materials. *For each student:*

◆ Student Sheets 3.1 and 3.2

◆ Cubical cereal box

◆ Leftover cardboard

◆ Scissors, centimeter ruler, scientific calculator

◆ Student Sheet 1.3 for reference

For each group of students:

◆ 100 unit cubes

◆ Masking tape

For the teacher:

◆ Two identical cereal boxes

◆ Transparency of Student Sheet 3.1 and a transparency pen

Getting Ready

1. Get two identical cereal boxes. Follow procedures in Activities 1 and 2 to construct a cubical box equivalent in volume to the other box.

2. Tape the leftover cardboard pieces together to form one or more rectangles. Calculate the area of the rectangles.

3. Duplicate Student Sheets 3.1 and 3.2.

4. Make a transparency of Student Sheet 3.1.

5. Locate scissors, centimeter rulers, scientific calculators, masking tape, centimeter cubes, and a transparency pen.

Background Information

As students complete their cubical cereal boxes in Activity 2, many may wonder about the leftover cardboard. Thinking they made an error in their construction process, some may reexamine their calculations for *E*, remeasure the square faces on their cubes for accuracy, and check their data. Once they realize everyone has leftover cardboard, they will accept their results: the cubical cereal box used less cardboard.

Student Sheet 3.1 explains the relationship between surface area and volume. Students build a 4 × 4 × 4 unit cube with sixty-four unit cubes (the volume) as shown in Figure A. By counting, they determine that the surface area of the cube is 96 square units. This represents the amount of cardboard necessary to build a box around the cube.

Students section their 4 × 4 × 4 cube into two 2 × 4 × 4 rectangular solids and then combine these into one 2 × 4 × 8 rectangular solid, similar to that shown in Figure B. There are different ways of reforming the rectangular solid: 2 × 4 × 8 and 2 × 8 × 4 are both acceptable responses. Note that while the total number of cubes remains sixty-four, there are more square faces visible and the surface area increases to 112 square units.

Figure A   Figure B

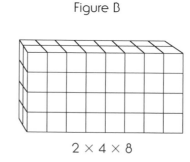

4 × 4 × 4   2 × 4 × 8

Figure C

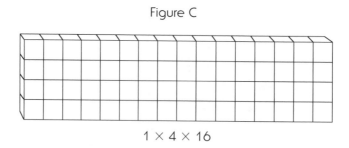

1 × 4 × 16

Students repeat this process, stretching the 2 × 4 × 8 or 2 × 8 × 4 rectangular solid into a 1 × 4 × 8 rectangular solid as shown in Figure C. The number of cubes is still sixty-four, but the surface area increases to 168 square units.

Dimensions	Volume in Cubic Units	Surface Area in Square Units
A: 4 × 4 × 4	64	96
B: 2 × 4 × 8	64	112
C: 1 × 4 × 16	64	168

On Student Sheet 3.2, students recognize the similarities and differences in the area of the leftover cardboard when it is calculated in two ways. First they tape the leftover pieces together to form one or more rectangles and calculate the area directly. Second they compare the surface area of their cubical cereal box to the surface area of their original box.

For the sample cereal box presented in Activity 1, the area of the rectangle representing the leftover cardboard is 359.0 square centimeters. The surface area of the sample cubical cereal box with $E = 15.8$ is 1,497.8 square centimeters. Since the surface area of the original cereal box was 1,864.6 square centimeters, the expected savings is 366.8 square centimeters. The two procedures represent a difference of 7.8 square centimeters, a 2 percent margin of error.

This difference occurs for a variety of reasons including inaccurate measurements, imprecise centimeter rulers, not piecing the rectangles together exactly, and losing pieces. Both solutions are valid representations of the approximate area of the leftover cardboard.

The Interest Link "Problems and Possibilities of Packaging" gives some of the actions states have taken to help reduce packaging waste. See the resource list for information on how to receive the Washington Packaging Task Force public education plan. See the Paul Underhill article in the resource list for more information on the controversy over compact disc packaging.

Presenting the Activity

Stretch Me. Divide your class into small groups and ask the following:

◆ After making your cubical cereal boxes, did you have leftover cardboard? Is this possible?

◆ Does your cubical cereal box hold the same amount of cereal as your original box? How do you know?

◆ Can two boxes have the same volume, but use different amounts of cardboard?

◆ How is the cardboard related to the surface area of a cereal box?

Hand out Student Sheet 3.1. Explain that this activity will help clarify and explain the relations between surface area and volume.

Distribute at least sixty-four unit cubes to each group and ask groups to build a 4 × 4 × 4 unit cube. Work with each group to carefully slide a 2 × 4 × 4 section of the cube and realign it with the remaining section to form a 2 × 4 × 8 rectangular solid. Then repeat the process, helping students form a 1 × 4 × 16 rectangular solid. Help them notice in their discussions that even though more squares become visible, the volume remains 64 cubic units.

After students have completed Student Sheet 3.1, display their data on a transparency of Student Sheet 3.1, and conduct a class discussion on their observations and conclusions.

It is now becoming clear that different rectangular solids with the same volume can have quite different surface areas. Since surface area affects the amount of cardboard needed to construct a cereal box and, therefore, the amount of waste produced, it is important to determine just how much cardboard the cubical cereal boxes save.

Show the class the two demonstration cereal boxes you prepared for comparison and to stimulate a discussion on both industrial and environmental reasons for and against manufacturing cubical cereal boxes.

Extra! Extra! Distribute Student Sheet 3.2. Each student calculates the area of his or her extra cardboard two ways. First they carefully tape the cardboard pieces together into rectangles. Some students may prefer to make two or more rectangles and then combine their areas. Next, students subtract the surface area of the cubical box from that of the original cereal box. Discuss ways to minimize error and come to consensus on acceptable margins of error.

Discuss with the class the problem of solid waste. Talk about the information provided in the Interest Link "Problems and Possibilities of Packaging." Ask students for their suggested solutions.

Student projects should remain in the classroom for further discussion and for Activity 4. The Writing Link activity, "The Origin of Cardboard," may be used at any time as an extension.

Discussion Questions

1. What does the leftover cardboard represent to you?

2. Of the two methods you used in Activity 3 to determine the amount of cardboard your cubical cereal box saves, which do you prefer? Which is the most accurate? Why?

3. Should cereal box companies make cubical cereal boxes? Explain.

4. Does everyone's cubical cereal box save the same amount of cardboard?

5. Do you think most people know that a cubical cereal box saves cardboard and therefore reduces waste?

6. Who might be interested in your results?

7. What are examples of other packaged items you think could be redesigned to save packaging material and therefore reduce the waste stream?

Assessment Strategies

1. Is the area of your extra cardboard less than, greater than, or equal to the area of one face of your cubical cereal box? Explain.

2. If the surface area of a cubical cereal box is $6E^2$, what is its volume? Explain your reasoning.

3. With your group, make a list of products you think are packaged with a minimal (small) amount of packaging material. Explain your reasoning.

4. Give the dimensions of five different rectangular solids, each with a volume of 24 cubic units. Determine the surface area of each solid.

Problems and Possibilities of Packaging

Packaging preserves food and protects merchandise. But it is also the largest single contributor to one of the most troubling environmental problems: solid waste. In 1990 packaging accounted for 30 percent of the municipal (town or city) solid waste stream—about 56.8 million tons of garbage. Only 13.8 million tons was recycled.

The municipal solid waste stream is defined as everything generated by a person or industry that produces waste or can become waste. All of the packaging produced is considered part of the solid waste stream even though some of it is recycled.

According to the United States Environmental Protection Agency (EPA), solid waste generation has more than doubled in the past three decades, from 88 million tons in 1960 to nearly 187.4 million tons in 1990. That equals 4 pounds of waste per person per day. By the year 2000 the total waste generated is expected to reach 216 million tons per year. The EPA has identified four ways to solve the solid waste problem. In order of importance they are: source reduction (less waste from the start), recycling, incineration, and landfilling.

Several corporations are demonstrating environmental consciousness in their packaging policies. Proctor and Gamble™, for instance, put their new concentrated Tide® in a nearly cubical box—an example of source reduction.

In 1989 the Washington State Legislature established a Packaging Task Force to evaluate methods to reduce the volume, weight, and toxicity of packaging entering the waste stream. Its members represent industry, government, environmental groups, and citizens.

The *Packaging Task Force Action Plan* provides policy makers a variety of approaches to effectively reduce packaging waste. The Force predicts that implementation of their plan will result in a 20 percent reduction of packaging by 1998. The group recommends that package manufacturers:

◆ design products and packaging that minimize waste and can be recycled.

◆ offer products in bulk or in concentrates where feasible and/or desirable.

◆ design packages for reuse or for refill where appropriate.

◆ reduce packaging weight and volume and eliminate or reduce toxic materials.

Indiana's packaging task force has also produced a document outlining goals for packaging reduction. Furthermore The Coalition of Northeast Governors (CNEG) has formed a Source Reduction Council. Their recommendations have been adopted in thirteen states.

Success in reducing excessive packaging depends on both consumers and manufacturers. Consumers, through what they purchase, can motivate manufacturers to change their practices. The Washington Packaging Task Force public education plan encourages consumers to

◆ select items with no packaging or minimum packaging whenever possible.

◆ compare packaging choices for a given product.

◆ buy nonperishable goods in larger packages.

◆ shop for recyclable packaging or packaging made of recycled material.

◆ shop for reusable containers.

◆ shop from bulk delivery systems.

The Origin of Cardboard

Where does cardboard come from? You may guess that cardboard is a form of paper, and paper comes from trees. But how does the huge trunk of a tree become transformed into a cereal box?

Research cardboard, logging, and paper to find information about the origin of cardboard. Learn about recycled cardboard. How does it differ from "new" cardboard? Write a short essay about how cardboard is produced, some of its many uses, and what problems or advantages are created by manufacturing cardboard.

Stretch Me

1. With your group, build a 4 × 4 × 4 unit cube.

2. Count the number of unit cubes to determine the volume of the 4 × 4 × 4 unit cube. Record your results in the table.

3. Calculate the surface area of the 4 × 4 × 4 unit cube and record your results in the table.

Dimensions	Volume in Cubic Units	Surface Area in Square Units
4 × 4 × 4		
2 × 4 ×		

4. Slide a 2 × 4 × 4 section of the large cube and realign it with the remaining section to form another rectangular solid. The dimensions of this rectangular solid are _____. Record them in the table above.

5. Calculate and record the volume of this new rectangular solid in the table. How does its volume compare with the volume of the 4 × 4 × 4 unit cube? Explain.

6. Does the surface area of this new rectangular solid appear to be the same as the 4 × 4 × 4 unit cube? Explain.

7. By counting the squares you see on each face, find the surface area of the new rectangular solid and record your results in the table.

8. Repeat this "stretching" idea again to form another rectangular solid. The dimensions of this solid are _____. Record results in the table.

9. How do the volume and surface area appear to have changed?

10. By counting, find the volume and surface area of this new rectangular solid and record them in the table.

11. What can you conclude from this activity?

Extra! Extra!

1. Compared to your original cereal box, how much will your new cubical cereal box hold? Explain.

2. One way to determine the amount of extra cardboard is to carefully tape the leftover pieces together to form one or more rectangles and then calculate the area of the rectangles.

    a. Tape your extra cardboard together.

    b. Sketch a picture of your rectangle(s) and label the dimensions.

    c. Calculate the area of your extra cardboard.

3. Why would a company consider packaging cereal in cubical boxes?

4. Another way to determine the amount of extra cardboard is to calculate the surface area of your cubical cereal box and compare it to the surface area of your original box.

   a. Calculate the surface area of your cubical cereal box.

   b. The surface area of your original cereal box was _____.

   c. Find the difference in the surface areas of your original cereal box and your new cubical cereal box.

   d. Using this method, the area of your extra cardboard is:

5. You have calculated the amount of extra cardboard using two different methods. Are the results the same? Should they be? Explain.

6. The cubical cereal box saves approximately _____ square centimeters of cardboard. Explain your reasoning.

7. Cardboard comes from _____. If you are saving cardboard, then

   you are saving _____.

ACTIVITY
4

PERCENTS AND PACKAGING

Overview

Students work with proportions and examine the role of percents in expressing and clarifying mathematical relationships. They determine the percent of cardboard their cubical cereal box saves. The leftover cardboard also represents a percent of the cardboard required to construct another cubical cereal box of equal volume. They discover this is a different percent than the percent saved. Students learn about the percent of paper products used for packaging in the United States and how it compares to the usage of other packaging materials. At the same time, they see that this paper represents yet a different percent of the items that contribute to the municipal solid waste stream.

Purpose. Students use proportions to determine the percent of cardboard the cubical cereal box saves. They extend their concept of percent to understand that the leftover cardboard can be a certain percent of their original box and yet represent a different percent of their cubical cereal box. They are able to see their role as an informed consumer.

Time. One to two 45-minute periods.

Materials. *For each student:*

◆ Student Sheets 4.1–4.4 and Student Sheet 3.2 (for reference)

◆ Scientific calculator

For the teacher:

◆ Demonstration cereal boxes from Activity 3

◆ Rectangle formed by taping together the leftover cardboard pieces

◆ Transparency Masters 4.5–4.7 and a transparency pen

Getting Ready

1. Duplicate Student Sheets 4.1–4.4.

2. Make Transparency Masters 4.5–4.7.

3. Locate scientific calculators, masking tape, and a transparency pen.

Background Information

Percents are used everywhere in our society, yet people often find the concept troublesome.

This activity provides a relevant use of percent as students determine the percent of cardboard each cubical cereal box saves. Because they have a common base of 100, percents standardize mathematical relationships and situations to make comparisons easier. In Activity 3 students found the differences in the surface areas of the two cereal boxes to get a numerical value that represented the amount of cardboard the cubical cereal box saved. In this activity they convert these results into a percent of savings.

There are several familiar algorithms for analyzing percent problems. This module recommends using a proportion as a strategy for solving percent situations. This strategy makes sense because it is based on the meaning of percent.

Percent is a name, as in *ten* or *million*. Percent is derived from two words: per meaning "part" and cent meaning "hundred." Percent is defined as "part of a hundred." Any percent can be converted to an equivalent ratio or decimal: $25\% = \frac{25}{100} = .25$.

Percent is a ratio with a base of a hundred. If two ratios, rates, or fractions are equivalent, you can form a proportion. In a proportion the cross-products are equivalent.

a. $\quad \dfrac{2}{3} = \dfrac{4}{6}$

$2 \cdot 6 = 3 \cdot 4$

$12 = 12$

b. $\quad \dfrac{5}{8} = \dfrac{25}{40}$

$5 \cdot 40 = 8 \cdot 25$

$200 = 200$

You can use this property to solve proportions in which one member is unknown.

c. $\quad \dfrac{3}{4} = \dfrac{x}{32}$

$3 \cdot 32 = 4 \cdot x$

$96 = 4x$

$24 = x$

d. $\quad \dfrac{3}{5} = \dfrac{p}{100}$

$3 \cdot 100 = 5 \cdot p$

$300 = 5p$

$60 = p$

$\dfrac{3}{5} = 60\%$

Through Student Sheets 4.1 and 4.2, students review a method for applying proportions to solving percent problems.

The packaging industry uses percents extensively. Percents give meaning to statements such as "If you are an average American, 33 percent of your garbage is packaging you toss out immediately," and "About 50 percent of paper in the United States is used solely for packaging." Percents can clarify complex situations and provide the basis for proposals to alter packaging methods and materials. See the Earth Works publication in the resource list (page xiii) for more on this.

In Student Sheets 4.3 and 4.4, students calculate various percents connected with saving cardboard when they use cubical boxes. For example, the surface area of the sample cereal box referred to earlier was 1,864.6 square centimeters, and the resulting cubical cereal box was 1,497.84 square centimeters. The sample cubical cereal box saves 366.76 square centimeters, a savings of almost 20 percent of the packaging.

Percent of Original Cardboard Saved By Sample Cubical Cereal Box

$$\frac{p}{100} = \frac{\text{Area of Leftover Cardboard}}{\text{Surface Area Original Box}}$$

$$\frac{p}{100} = \frac{366.76}{1864.6}$$

$$1,864.6p = 36,676$$

$$p = 19.6696$$

$$\frac{p}{100} = \frac{19.7}{100} = 20\%$$

The saved cardboard can be used toward constructing an additional cubical cereal box. The percent this cardboard represents of the material necessary to build a second equivalent cubical cereal box exceeds 24 percent.

Percent of Cubical Cereal Box the Savings Represents

$$\frac{p}{100} = \frac{\text{Area of Extra Cardboard}}{\text{Surface Area Cubical Box}}$$

$$\frac{p}{100} = \frac{366.73}{1497.84}$$

$$1,497.84p = 36,676$$

$$p = 24.4859$$

$$\frac{p}{100} = \frac{24.48}{100} = 24\%$$

Use Transparency Master 4.5 to show the amount of leftover cardboard for some of the students. The data will most likely show that the amount of leftover cardboard varies considerably from student to student. You should expect this if students bring different-sized boxes. The amount of cardboard in each box differs depending on its size and shape. What is interesting is that the percent of cardboard saved will most likely range between 15 and 24 percent.

Look at Transparency Master 4.6. It identifies by percent the specific materials that are the major components of packaging in the United States. Over 27 million tons of paper for packaging purposes were generated in 1990. Transparency Master 4.6 shows that paper comprised 47.7 percent of all packaging material in 1990, yet it represented only 15 percent of all municipal waste as shown in Transparency Master 4.7. The same amount of paper can be represented as different percents.

At the conclusion of Activity 4, the class uses their percent data to predict the number of extra cubical cereal boxes that could be produced by combining all of their leftover cardboard. For example, the thirty-two original cereal boxes when reconstructed become thirty-two cubical cereal boxes of equal volume plus, perhaps, eight additional cubical cereal boxes of similar volume.

Presenting the Activity

Proportions to Percents. Divide your class into small groups. Ask them for examples of how percents are used in the newspaper, in magazines, in stores, on television, and in other facets of life. Examples may include, "contains 20 percent fruit juice," "40 percent of Americans . . . ," and "a 2 percent raise." Because percents are commonly used, it is important to understand and be able to work with them.

Define *percent* as a word name, as in *ten* or *million*, that is used with numbers. Percent means "part of a hundred." One percent, or 1%, means "one part of a hundred" or "one-hundredth," which can be written as $\frac{1}{100}$. The percent symbol (%) illustrates hundredths. Twenty-five parts of a hundred can be written as a ratio, $\frac{25}{100}$, or as a percent, 25%.

Explain how in mathematics there is usually more than one method to solve a problem. One way to resolve a percent problem is to use proportions. A proportion states that two fractions or ratios are equivalent, such as $\frac{1}{2} = \frac{3}{6}$.

Proportional Thinking. Hand out Student Sheet 4.1. Discuss with the class how proportions are made by setting two equivalent ratios equal to each other. Have them make the requested proportions. As you observe the groups, make sure they understand how to form cross products and the relation between them. If necessary discuss cross products.

When students have finished, conduct a class discussion to demonstrate their methods for finding a missing member in a proportion and to determine acceptable formats.

Hand out Student Sheet 4.2. Students explore a method for using proportions to solve percent problems. Suggest that they communicate ideas within their group as they work through each problem. Before they begin, conduct an informal class survey to get a count representing the number of students who would prefer to eat raisin bran cereal for breakfast rather than shredded wheat cereal. Record this information on the chalkboard or overhead, and inform them that problem 4 on Student Sheet 4.2 uses this data.

Discuss methods of solution and conclusions to problems 4 and 5 on Student Sheet 4.2 where students set up and use proportions to solve for unknown percents.

What Percent of Cardboard Was Saved? Distribute Student Sheet 4.3. In this activity students find the percent of cardboard that their cubical cereal box saves. Before they begin, ask the class to refer to Student Sheet 3.2 and decide which method they feel gives the most accurate representation for the area of their leftover cardboard. Based on the response, suggest that they record this area for problem 1 on Student Sheet 4.3.

After the groups have finished exchanging and analyzing information, discuss with the class whether there is any consistent pattern in the percent of cardboard a cubical cereal box saves.

Put up Transparency Master 4.5 and record the percent of cardboard the cubical box saved by selected students or groups. Discuss the similarities and variations in the percents. Ask students:

◆ What affects the differences in the percents?

◆ Are the percents similar? In what way?

On Student Sheet 4.4, students determine what percent the extra cardboard represents of the cardboard needed to construct a cubical cereal box of equal volume.

This activity illustrates how the leftover cardboard represents at least two different percents of cardboard. The percent depends on whether you are comparing it to the amount of cardboard in the original cereal box

(Student Sheet 4.3) or the cardboard used in the cubical cereal box (Student Sheet 4.4). Spend time debating the percent of savings between various cereal boxes in order to predict the number of extra cubical cereal boxes the class could provide.

Percents in Packaging. Put Transparency Master 4.6 on the overhead. Explain that the pie chart represents all of the packages made in the United States in 1990. It is divided into wedges that show what percent of the packages were made of certain materials. For example, 24.5 percent of the packages were glass. Most packages., 47.7 percent, were made of paper. That percent represents over 27 million tons of paper.

Now put up Transparency Master 4.7. Explain that this pie chart shows the breakdown of what garbage we produce. Define *municipal* (of a city or town) and *solid waste* (garbage) for your students. Point out that 30.3 percent of the waste is packaging materials. This 30.3 percent represents the entire pie chart on Transparency Master 4.6. Help students understand how an item can represent a particular percent when compared to one thing, but a different percent when compared to something else. The Writing Link "Up to Our Waists in Waste" can be used any time during the activity to get students thinking about the problem of waste disposal.

Discussion Questions

1. What have you learned from this module so far?

2. How do percents help clarify the information in this module?

3. Take home your cubical box and extra cardboard along with your data and work showing that a cubical cereal box of equal volume uses less packaging than the standard cereal box. Discuss your procedures and results with your family or some other adult. Describe their reactions in a one-page written report.

Assessment Strategies

1. Interpret and discuss this statement: My cubical cereal box used 20 percent less cardboard than my original cereal box, and this savings is 25 percent of the cardboard I need to build a second cubical cereal box.

   Is this statement believable? Explain.

2. If a company designs a cubical single-serving cereal box, what percent of the cardboard would this save?

3. How much cardboard would be saved in an entire variety pack of ten single-serving cereal boxes?

Up to Our Waists in Waste

The next time you throw a piece of paper away, think about this: where is it going to go? We create garbage faster than we can get rid of it and so it piles up. Many landfills are stuffed and either there is no more land available to build another one, or people fight about where to build it. (Do you want a trash dump in your backyard?)

How are we going to solve the problem? Should we load it into a space shuttle and toss it on the moon? Maybe we should dig deeper, fill the holes with trash, then build a park over the top while we wait for a hundred years until the stuff decays (of course, some of it will never decay). Or perhaps we should stop throwing things away so quickly and learn to recycle.

Research waste disposal, recycling, and other aspects of our garbage problem. Then write a short essay giving your solution. Include how and why you think your solution would work.

Proportional Thinking

1. If two ratios are equivalent you can form them into a proportion.

   For example: $\dfrac{1}{3} = \dfrac{2}{6}$

   Write at least three more proportions using ratios equivalent to $\dfrac{1}{3}$.

2. Write at least three proportions using the ratio $\dfrac{2}{5}$.

3. Write at least three proportions using the ratio $\dfrac{8}{7}$.

4. In the proportion $\dfrac{1}{2} = \dfrac{3}{6}$ the cross products are represented by 1×6 and 2×3.

   Follow the process in this example to evaluate the cross products for each of your proportions in questions 1–3.

   Examine and compare your cross products. What do you notice?

5. Discuss with your group how to use cross products to solve this proportion. Solve it.

$$\frac{3}{4} = \frac{x}{32}$$

6. Use cross products to solve the following proportions:

a. $\frac{3}{15} = \frac{a}{25}$

b. $\frac{7}{4} = \frac{35}{x}$

c. $\frac{4}{n} = \frac{12}{15}$

d. $\frac{2}{5} = \frac{p}{100}$

7. Now write your own proportion problem and solve it using cross products.

Proportions, Products, and Percents

1. Percent is defined as part of 100. Convert these percents to ratios with a base of 100.

   25% =   130% = x% =

2. Convert these ratios to percents.

   $\dfrac{18}{100} =$ $\dfrac{2}{100} =$ $\dfrac{p}{100} =$

3. On a separate piece of paper, set up proportions, use cross products, and convert these ratios to percents.

   $\dfrac{9}{20} = \dfrac{p}{100}$ $\dfrac{3}{8} =$ $\dfrac{8}{5} =$

4. There are _____ students in class today. Find out how many would prefer raisin bran to shredded wheat for breakfast: _____. Use proportions to calculate the percent of students that prefer raisin bran.

5. If 780,000 tons of cardboard are used this year for packaging, and 187,200 tons of it are thrown away, what percent may be recycled?

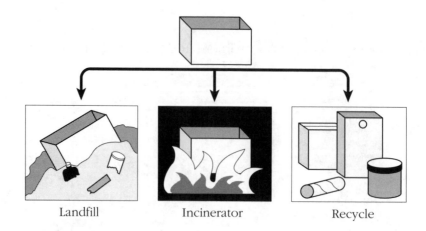

Landfill   Incinerator   Recycle

Imagine That!

1. Your leftover cardboard equals _____ square centimeters.

2. Use a proportion and solve for p to find the percent your leftover cardboard represents of the cardboard required by the original cereal box. Round your solution to the nearest whole percent.

$$\frac{p}{100} = \frac{\text{Area of Leftover Cardboard}}{\text{Surface Area Original Box}}$$

3. A cubical cereal box would save _____ % of the cardboard

   used by the _____ company to package their cereal.

4. Is this a significant amount? Explain.

5. Fill in the table by collecting information from people in your group and in another group.

Student Name	Area of Leftover Cardboard (in cm)	Percent of Cardboard the Cubical Cereal Box Saves
1.		
2.		
3.		
4.		
5.		
6.		
7.		

6. Do cubical cereal boxes of different sizes save similar percents of cardboard? Explain.

Imagine This!

1. How does the area of the rectangle made with your leftover cardboard compare visually with the total amount of cardboard used to make your cubical cereal box?

2. Percents provide another way to express this comparison. Set up a proportion to find the percent of leftover cardboard to the cardboard used to build your cubical cereal box. Round your solution to the nearest whole percent.

3. A cubical cereal box has _____ congruent faces. Therefore one face is what fractional part of the cube? _____

4. Set up and solve a proportion to convert the above fractional part to the nearest whole percent.

5. One face of a cubical cereal box is _____ % of the cardboard needed to construct it. The rectangle you made with the leftover cardboard

   represents _____ % of the cardboard required to construct a cubical cereal box. What do you notice?

6. There are _____ students in your class. If your classmates' results are similar to yours, then approximately how many additional cubical cereal boxes could you construct using everyone's extra pieces? Explain this.

Comparison Table

Student Name	Area of Leftover Cardboard (in cm)	Percent of Cardboard Cubical Cereal Box Saves
1.		
2.		
3.		
4.		
5.		
6.		
7.		
8.		
9.		
10.		
11.		
12.		
13.		
14.		
15.		
16.		
17.		
18.		
19.		
20.		
21.		
22.		
23.		
24.		
25.		
26.		
27.		
28.		
29.		
30.		
31.		
32.		

United States Packaging Materials, 1990

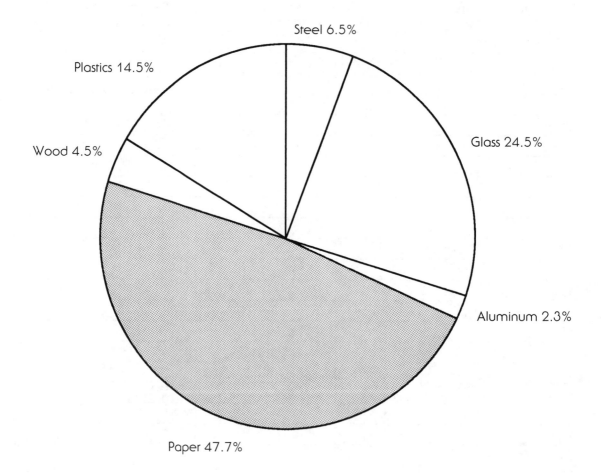

Steel 6.5%

Plastics 14.5%

Glass 24.5%

Wood 4.5%

Aluminum 2.3%

Paper 47.7%

Components of Municipal Solid Waste

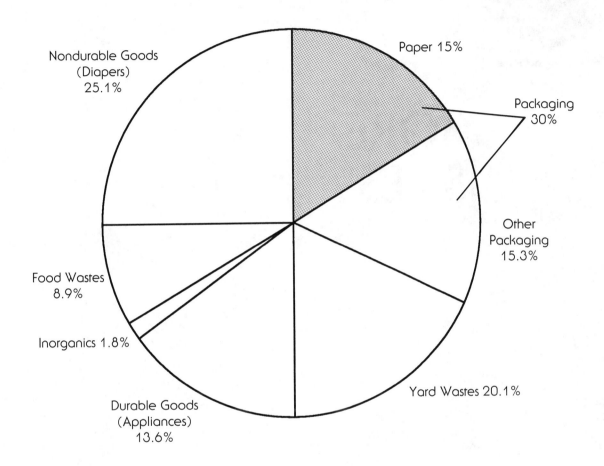

ACTIVITY 5

MORE IS LESS

Overview

Students hypothesize and discover how much a cubical cereal box with a side that is twice the length of their existing cubical cereal box will hold, and how much cardboard this large-size cereal box requires. They incorporate their results into packaging and consumer strategies for waste reduction.

Purpose. Students determine the surface area and volume relationship when the dimensions of a rectangular solid are doubled. They use this information to explore purchasing alternatives and their effect on the environment.

Time. One to two 45-minute periods.

Materials. *For each student:*
- Student Sheets 5.1 and 5.2
- Scientific calculator
- Student Sheets 1.3 and 2.1 (for reference)

For each group of students:
- 100 one-unit cubes

For the teacher:
- Demonstration cereal boxes from Activity 3
- 7 additional student-made cubical cereal boxes close to the same dimensions as the one made in Activity 3 and a marker or tape
- Enough cardboard to construct a cubical cereal box double the dimensions of your demonstration cubical cereal box

Getting Ready

1. Make a cubical cereal box model with dimensions twice those of your demonstration cubical cereal box.
2. Locate seven additional cubical cereal boxes from the class's with approximately the same dimensions as your demonstration box for a total of eight cubical boxes
3. Duplicate Student Sheets 5.1 and 5.2.
4. Locate scientific calculators and cubes.

Background Information

One responsibility of the Washington State Packaging Task Force is to teach professionals and consumers how to reduce waste. One recommendation is to buy nonperishable goods in large-size packages.

Students will discover in Activity 5 that a large-size cubical cereal box made by doubling the length of each edge of a regular-size cubical cereal box requires four times as much cardboard; yet it can hold eight times as much cereal. See Completed Student Sheet 5.1 (page 89) for an example of this. If you could purchase a large-size cubical cereal box designed in this fashion, it would be equivalent to buying eight regular-size cubical cereal boxes; yet it would only require the amount of cardboard to construct four regular cubical cereal boxes, saving a significant amount of the cardboard packaging.

This activity shows how the surface area and the volume change with respect to increasing the dimensions of a rectangular solid by a given factor. In this case, the factor is purposely limited to two in order to promote a clear understanding of what is often an overwhelming concept to middle-school students.

Extending the concept to factors greater than two is not recommended at this time; but if the length of each edge is multiplied by a factor of 3, then the surface area is 3^2, or 9 times as great, and the volume is 3^3, or 27, times as large. In general, increasing the dimensions by a factor of x changes the surface area by a factor of x^2 and the volume by a factor of x^3.

If you were to make a large cubical cereal box by doubling the length of each edge of the sample cubical cereal box, you would find that the surface area increases by a factor of four; yet it will hold eight times as much.

Sample Cereal Box

Cubical Cereal Box	Length of E	Surface Area	Volume
Regular-size	~15.8 cm	1,497.8 square cm	3,939 cubic cm
Large-size	~31.6 cm	5,991.4 square cm	31,554 cubic cm

The volume of the regular-size cubical cereal box above is approximately 3,939 cubic centimeters. Eight of these boxes will provide 3,939 × 8 or 31,512 cubic centimeters of cereal. It requires approximately 1,497.8 square centimeters of cardboard to construct one of these boxes. Eight of them will use 1,497.8 × 8 or 11,982.7 square centimeters of packaging.

It will require 11,982.7 square centimeters of cardboard to construct the eight regular-size cereal boxes approximately equivalent in volume to one large-size cereal box that uses only 5,991.4 square centimeters of cardboard. This is half the packaging needed to construct the eight regular-size cubical cereal boxes. With equal volumes, a large-size box would save 50 percent of the packaging material required to construct eight regular cereal boxes.

$$\frac{p}{100} = \frac{5991.36}{11982.72}$$

$$11982.72p = 59.9136$$

$$p = 50$$

$$\frac{p}{100} = \frac{50}{100} = 50\%$$

This would be a good day to invite a packaging engineer or an environmentalist familiar with the concepts of waste reduction and packaging to your class(es) to participate in this activity and to facilitate further discussions on the ideas presented in this module.

Presenting the Activity

Cereal Boxes in the Store. Divide your students into small groups. Ask students the following questions:

◆ What different sizes of cereal boxes can you buy in a store?

◆ Usually you can buy a brand of cereal in at least two different sizes, perhaps a regular- or large-size box. Why is this?

◆ Why would someone choose to buy the large-size cereal box?

◆ How much more do you suppose a large-size cereal box holds than a regular-size cereal box?

Ask students to imagine that the cubical cereal box they made was a regular-size cereal box. Now ask the following:

◆ What would happen if you made a large-size cubical cereal box by doubling the length of each edge of your regular-size cubical box?

◆ How much cardboard do you think your large-size cubicle cereal box will need?

◆ How much cereal do you think it will hold?

Record their responses and hypotheses on the chalkboard or overhead and refer to these during the discussions following their completion of Student Sheets 5.1 and 5.2.

Remind students that the amount of cardboard represents the box's surface area and the volume is a measure of how much it holds.

More or Less. Distribute Student Sheet 5.1 to each student and about a hundred unit cubes to each group. Explain that they are going to investigate these questions using the cubes to construct models of different-sized cereal boxes. They will interpret data about the surface area and volume of various cubes when the length of each side is doubled. After they have analyzed their data and noticed patterns, they will be ready to draw conclusions about the increase in surface area and volume.

After students have completed and discussed the relationship between surface area and volume as a function of increasing dimension within their groups, you may want to conduct a brief class discussion using a transparency of Student Sheet 5.1 to present their results and review the class's perceptions of the data and its suggested conclusions.

More Is Less. Distribute Student Sheet 5.2 and observe the group interactions as they apply the concepts derived from Student Sheet 5.1 to the actual process of doubling the length of each side on their own cubical cereal box.

When they have completed Student Sheet 5.2, display your demonstration cubical cereal box and the large-size cubical model you created by doubling its dimensions. Use this to generate further discussion and to show that the large-size model will indeed hold eight of your cubical cereal boxes. Either use eight similar cubical boxes from the class or use the one demonstration cubical box and a marker to show how eight of them would fit in the large-size box. Masking tape serves as a good marker in this demonstration.

Have a class discussion to summarize and review the following aspects of this module:

◆ Different rectangular solids with the same volume can have different surface areas.

◆ A cubical cereal box saves cardboard and reduces the waste stream.

◆ Doubling the length of each edge of a cubical cereal box requires four times as much cardboard, yet provides eight times as much cereal.

Discussion Questions

1. Did the results of this activity surprise you?

2. Would you recommend that people buy food/cereal in large-size containers, when possible? Explain.

3. Do you recommend that companies make large-size cubical cereal boxes? Explain.

4. Discuss the Interest Link "Real-life Waste Savers." Exactly what did this company do to help the environment? Can you think of benefits of this company's practices other than what were listed? Are there disadvantages?

Assessment Strategies

1. Suppose you were to design a small-size cereal box by cutting the edge length of your existing cubical cereal box in half. Predict how the surface area and the volume of this smaller version would change in relation to your regular cubical cereal box. Describe the basis for your conclusions.

2. Calculate the dimensions for a cubical cereal box that would be double the volume of your existing cubical cereal box. Determine its surface area and compare it to the surface area of your existing box.

3. If the length of each side of your regular-size cereal box is tripled, by what percent is the surface area increased? the volume?

Help-the-Environment Store

Imagine a grocery store that encourages its customers to help the environment. From the products it sells to the bags it uses for packing the groceries, this store tries to do everything right. Research recycling, packaging, and pollution to find ways a store could help the environment. Think about the following:

◆ What size packages would be most common? What packaging materials would be allowed on the shelves?

◆ What products would or would not be sold here?

◆ How would customers get to the store?

◆ How would the store be lighted, heated, or cooled?

◆ What special features would this store have to encourage recycling?

◆ What materials would be used to make the carts, shelves, and decorations?

◆ How would the groceries be packed and in what?

Write a short essay describing your store in detail. Give it a name and a slogan. You may even want to draw a picture of the store's layout to show its features.

Real-life Waste Savers

Some companies make extra efforts to help the solid waste crisis. For example, one small but growing health and beauty product company has made concern for the environment part of its selling strategy. What does it do?

First, the company uses as little packaging as possible. There are no outside cartons. Also, for most of their products, you can refill your bottles at the store for a discount price. This saves you money since you do not have to buy a new plastic bottle. It also helps the environment because you are reusing something that would have otherwise ended up in an overcrowded garbage dump.

Even the bags in which the salesperson puts your purchases are made of recycled paper and have environmental messages printed on them. The company is also working on creating new materials that will decompose in garbage dumps instead of sitting there forever as plastic bottles do.

This company has been very successful, partly because people are beginning to buy products that do not add to our environmental problems. If more companies followed this example, and if more people bought only recyclable or reduced-waste packages, it would be an excellent step in improving the earth instead of destroying it.

More or Less

1. What do you think will happen to the surface area and volume of a cube if you double its dimensions?

2. Begin with a 1 × 1 × 1 unit cube. Record its surface area and volume in the table.

3. Double the length of each side to build a 2 × 2 × 2 unit cube. Determine the surface area and volume. Record your results in the table.

   a. Did the surface area double? Explain.

   b. Did the volume double? Explain.

4. Double the length of each side again and build a 4 × 4 × 4 unit cube. Predict the

   surface area: _____ and the volume: _____.

5. Calculate the surface area and volume of a 4 × 4 × 4 unit cube. Record your results in the table.

   a. Is there a pattern in how the surface area is changing? Explain.

   b. Is the volume changing in the same way? Explain.

6. Record the surface area and volume for an 8 × 8 × 8 unit cube.

Unit Cube Size	Surface Area in Square Units	Volume in Cubic Units
1 × 1 × 1		
2 × 2 × 2		
4 × 4 × 4		
8 × 8 × 8		

7. Based on these results, write a conclusion that describes what happens to the surface area and volume of a cube when you double the length of each side.

More Is Less

1. Cereal can often be purchased in at least two different sizes—regular and large. For this activity, consider your cubical cereal box to be a regular-size cereal box. If you double the length of each edge of your regular-size cereal box to construct a large-size cereal box, predict how much cardboard you would need to build it. How much cereal will it hold?

2. In the table below, record the data for your regular-size cereal box by referring to Student Sheets 1.3 and 2.1.

3. Determine and record the length for each edge of your large-size cereal box by doubling the edge length of your regular-size cereal box.

4. Calculate and record the surface area and volume for your large-size cubical cereal box.

Cubical Cereal Box	Length of Each Edge	Surface Area	Volume
Regular-size			
Large-size			

5. When you double the length of each edge of a cereal box it takes

_____ times as much cardboard to construct it, and the cereal box

will hold _____ times as much cereal! Explain how more is less.

6. If you are concerned about the environment and want to conserve our natural resources and reduce waste, does it matter which size cereal box you buy? Explain.

FAMILY
ACTIVITY

CEREAL
BOX

Overview

Students and their families use exactly one sheet of cardstock paper to construct a cereal box they think will hold the most cereal possible.

Purpose. Students and their families apply the concepts of this module and their ingenuity toward designing the most efficient cereal box, a box that maximizes the volume for the given surface area.

Time. At least one hour.

Materials. *For each student*

◆ Family Activity Sheet 1

◆ One 8.5" × 11" sheet of cardstock

For each family group:

◆ 8.5" × 11" practice paper

◆ Scientific calculator

◆ Scissors

◆ Tape

◆ Centimeter ruler

For the teacher:

◆ A full box of cereal

◆ 4-cup graduated transparent measuring cup

Getting Ready

1. Locate 8.5" × 11" cardstock paper.

2. Buy a box of compact cereal such as Grapenuts® or oatmeal.

3. Find a 4-cup graduated transparent measuring cup.

4. Duplicate Family Activity Sheet 1.

Background Information

This activity lets students show their families what they have learned about surface area, volume relationships, and waste-reduction issues. Note: If students do not have a family with which they can do the experiment, give them the option of working with a group of other students or joining with another student's family.

In this module, students were given a constant volume and determined that a cube used the minimum surface area for a rectangular solid. Surface area was the variable. Now they are asked to construct a cereal box out of a sheet of cardstock paper that provides the maximum volume. The surface area remains constant, and the volume becomes the variable.

This module has restricted its investigations to rectangular solids. As the module has shown, the cube is the most efficient rectangular solid, providing the maximum volume for minimum surface area. Many will choose to design the cube with the maximum volume, but others may wonder if there is an even more efficient shape and want to investigate this. Therefore do not restrict students' designs to rectangular solids or containers for which they can mathematically calculate the precise volume. The volume of their boxes will be determined by how much cereal they hold.

The most efficient rectangular solid design based on the given surface area can be determined by solving for E, the length of one edge of a cube, using the surface area formula below.

$$\text{Surface Area} = 6E^2$$
$$8.5'' \times 11'' = 93.5 \text{ in.}^2 = 6E^2$$
$$15.58 \text{ in.}^2 = E^2$$
$$3.9 \text{ in.} = E$$

Family Activity Sheet 1 lists the materials needed and gives directions for doing the activity.

Presenting the Activity

Cereal Box. Divide your class into small groups. Hand out Family Activity Sheet 1 and have students discuss it in their groups. Make sure students understand how this activity differs from their construction of a cubical box that held the same amount of cereal as before. Help them understand they are to construct a container that will hold the most cereal possible.

Ask students to consider these design criteria.

◆ The final product must be stable.

◆ The edges of the "box" should not have gaps or overlapping cardboard.

◆ The container must be closed but have an opening.

Give students a reasonable length of time, perhaps four or five days spanning a weekend, to complete the assignment.

On the day the cereal boxes are due, set up a demonstration area in the classroom to observe and discuss each family's construction. Ask the class which models they think have the greatest volume and why. Use compact cereal such as Grapenuts® and a graduated measuring cup to determine which box holds the most cereal.

Students can complete the Writing Link activity "Design Your Box Cover" at home with their families or in class.

Discussion Questions

1. How do you know you have constructed a container that holds the most cereal possible?

2. Does your box look like a box you might find on a grocery shelf?

3. Do you think you could convince your favorite cereal company to use your design?

4. What was the most interesting thing you learned from this activity?

5. How many drafts did you make before you decided on your box?

Design Your Box Cover

After you finish creating the new cereal box with your family, think about how it would look on the grocery store shelf. Will your little box stand out among the colorful packages offering prizes and healthy flakes?

Imagine your packaging engineer supervisor has told you this box will carry a new brand of wheat flake cereal. You must come up with a design idea for each face of the box to present to the artists. The box should communicate the following:

◆ The box is a new design for environmentally conscious consumers. It offers the most cereal with the lowest packaging waste.

◆ These are new, better-tasting wheat flakes.

◆ The company name and address (you make up).

◆ The ingredients and nutrition information (you make up).

Be creative! Use shapes, pictures, colors, and lettering to make a cereal box that will practically leap into customers' shopping carts. Either make a design on paper or put it directly on the box. Write a few paragraphs explaining why you picked the design you did and why you think customers will buy the cereal.

Cereal Box

You and your family are to construct a cereal box out of one sheet of cardstock paper. Construct the box so that it holds the maximum amount of cereal possible. In the activity you did in class, you constructed a cubical box that kept the volume constant but had a reduced surface area. In this activity, you keep the surface area constant and create a box with maximum volume.

There is no restriction on the design of your container, and you do not need to know how to mathematically calculate its precise volume. The volume of your box will be determined by how much cereal it holds. When you have completed the box, you will take it to class and your teacher will determine its volume.

Below are the materials you will need and the directions for doing the activity. Discuss these with your family. Since the cardstock is the size of a standard piece of notebook paper, you may use as many practice sheets as you and your family deem necessary. Construction paper works better than notebook paper.

The cereal box you develop must be completely closed, but have a portion that opens sufficiently to pour cereal in and out of it.

Materials you will need
◆ One 8.5" × 11" sheet of cardstock
◆ 8.5" × 11" practice paper, construction paper, if possible
◆ Tape
◆ Scissors
◆ Scientific calculator
◆ Centimeter ruler

Making the Box
1. Make and test as many practice designs as you wish using standard notebook paper (or construction paper) that has the same area as one sheet of cardstock paper. Wait to use the cardstock until you are sure of the construction you want to present to the class.

2. Remember, even though you have only learned the volume and surface area formulas for rectangular solids, you can experiment using any shape or combination of shapes. Your goal is to find the shape that can hold the most cereal.

3. Make a sketch of your final container, and predict how much cereal your container will hold.

4. Bring your container to class on the day it is due. All the boxes will be tested in class to demonstrate which one holds the most cereal.

COMPLETED
STUDENT
SHEETS

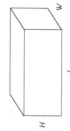

COMPLETED STUDENT SHEET 1.1

Fill It Up

1. Fill the single-serving cereal box with centimeter cubes to find the maximum number of cubes it can hold. *It can hold 280 centimeter cubes.*

2. Based on the total number of cubes the single-serving cereal box holds, the volume of this rectangular solid is ___*280 cubic cm*___.

3. Volume is measured in what kind of units? ___*cubic units*___

4. Explain your process for determining the number of cubes needed to fill the cereal box.
   Answers will vary.

5. How many cubes are in one layer? ___*70*___

6. How many layers of these cubes fit in the single-serving cereal box?
   ___*4*___

7. What is the height of your box in centimeters? ___*4*___

8. Use the cubes to determine the other dimensions in centimeters of the single-serving cereal box.

   Length ___*10*___ Width ___*7*___

COMPLETED STUDENT SHEET 1.1 (cont'd)

9. Write an equation to describe a relation between the length (*L*), width (*W*), and height (*H*) of a cereal box and its volume (*V*).
   Answers will vary but should be some form of $V = L \times W \times H$

10. If you are given the dimensions of a rectangular box, how would you calculate the total number of cubes it can hold? _____
   Answers will vary but the general sense should be to multiply the length by the width by the height.

5. Determine the area of each rectangle on the network. Fill in the table below.

Rectangle	Number of Squares	Dimensions (in cm) Length	Width	Area
Top	70*	10	7	70 sq cm
Bottom	70	10	7	70 sq cm
Front	40	10	4	40 sq cm
Back	40	10	4	40 sq cm
Left Side	28	7	4	28 sq cm
Right Side	28	7	4	28 sq cm
Total Surface Area				276 sq cm

Answers will vary depending on the orientation of the box.

6. Area is measured in what kind of units? ___square units___

7. If you are given the dimensions of a cereal box, how would you calculate its surface area?

Answers will vary. One possible response is: Find the area of each rectangular face and add them together.

8. What is the relationship between the wrapping-paper network and the amount of cardboard used to make the single-serving cereal box?

Answers will vary. However the general meaning should be to convey that they are approximately equivalent.

Wrap It Up

1. Trace each rectangular face of the single-serving cereal box onto a sheet of centimeter graph paper. This approximately equals the surface area. Outline the dimensions to the nearest centimeter.

2. Label the pieces on the graph paper to show a top, bottom, front, back, left side, and right side of the single-serving cereal box.

3. Cut out each rectangle. Using clear tape, tape them together to form a flat network that will cover each face when it is wrapped around the single-serving cereal box.

4. Sketch your wrapping-paper network below.

Answers will vary.

5. Cut open your cereal box along the seams to form a flat network. If you accidentally cut a section off, tape it back on. In the space provided, draw a picture of your network. Label the dimensions.

Answers will vary; however the sketches should be similar to the networks given on Student Sheet 1.2

6. Complete the table to determine the surface area of your cereal box.

Rectangle	Number of Squares	Dimensions (in cm) Length	Width	Area
Top	*Answers will vary*			
Bottom				
Front				
Back				
Left Side				
Right Side				
Total Surface Area				

7. Surface area is measured in _____ *square* _____ units.

Box Basics

1. Using a centimeter ruler, measure and record the dimensions of your own cereal box to the nearest tenth of a centimeter.

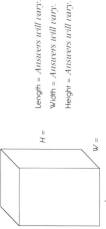

H =

W =

L =

Length = *Answers will vary.*

Width = *Answers will vary.*

Height = *Answers will vary.*

2. Calculate the volume of your cereal box using the formula for the volume of a rectangular solid.

$V = L \times W \times H$, but numerical answers will vary.

3. Volume is measured in _____ *cubic* _____ units.

4. How many centimeter cubes will fill your cereal box?

Answers will vary. However the response should be the same as the response to problem 2 allowing for rounding to whole numbers to accomodate cubes.

COMPLETED STUDENT SHEET 3.1

Stretch Me

1. With your group, build a $4 \times 4 \times 4$ unit cube.

2. Count the number of unit cubes to determine the volume of the $4 \times 4 \times 4$ unit cube. Record your results in the table.

3. Calculate the surface area of the $4 \times 4 \times 4$ unit cube and record your results in the table.

Dimensions	Volume in Cubic Units	Surface Area in Square Units
$4 \times 4 \times 4$	$64\ cm^3$	$96\ cm^2$
$2 \times 4 \times 8$ or $2 \times 8 \times 4^*$	$64\ cm^3$	$112\ cm^2$
$1 \times 4 \times 16$ or $1 \times 16 \times 4$	$64\ cm^3$	$168\ cm^2$

*Answers will vary depending on the orientation of the rectangular solid.

4. Slide a $2 \times 4 \times 4$ section of the large cube and realign it with the remaining section to form another rectangular solid. The dimensions of this rectangular solid are $2 \times 4 \times 8$ or $2 \times 8 \times 4$. Record them in the table above.

5. Calculate and record the volume of this new rectangular solid in the table. How does its volume compare with the volume of the $4 \times 4 \times 4$ unit cube? Explain. *The volume of the two rectangular solids is the same.*

COMPLETED STUDENT SHEET 2.1

The Root of It All

You are going to redesign your cereal box to make a cube that will hold the same amount of cereal.

1. The volume of your cereal box is *Answers will vary.*

2. What is a cube? *Answers will vary.*

3. What will be the volume of your new cubical cereal box? *Same as response to 1.*

4. The formula for the volume of a rectangular solid is $V = L \times W \times H$.

5. A special formula for the volume of a cube with dimension E is
$$V = E^3$$
.

6. Substitute the volume of your cereal box into the special formula for V. *Answers will vary.*

7. Use a scientific calculator to determine E by finding the cube root of both sides of the special formula.

$$\sqrt[3]{} = \sqrt[3]{}$$ *Answers will vary.*

8. Round the display to the nearest tenth of a centimeter.

$E =$ *Answers will vary.*

9. What does E tell you? *E is the length of one edge of a cubical cereal box that has the same volume as the cereal box I brought from home.*

10. Think about the process you will use to build your cube. Build it.

COMPLETED STUDENT SHEETS   **83**

Extra! Extra!

1. Compared to your original cereal box, how much will your new cubical cereal box hold? Explain.

   They both hold approximately the same amount of cereal.

2. One way to determine the amount of extra cardboard is to carefully tape the leftover pieces together to form one or more rectangles and then calculate the area of the rectangles.

   a. Tape your extra cardboard together.

   b. Sketch a picture of your rectangle(s) and label the dimensions.

      Answers will vary. They may make one, two, or possibly three rectangles, and there is no way to predict the dimensions of the rectangles.

   c. Calculate the area of your extra cardboard.

      Answers will vary. The amount of leftover cardboard will depend on the shape and size of the cereal box.

3. Why would a company consider packaging cereal in cubical boxes?

   Answers will vary. One possible response is: Cubical boxes that have the same volume as noncubical boxes require less cardboard, and making cubical boxes would save the company money.

---

6. Does the surface area of this new rectangular solid appear to be the same as the $4 \times 4 \times 4$ unit cube? Explain.

   The surface area of the noncubic rectangular solid appears to be greater than the surface area of the cube.

7. By counting the squares you see on each face, find the surface area of the new rectangular solid and record your results in the table.

8. Repeat this "stretching" idea again to form another rectangular solid. The dimensions of this solid are __$2 \times 4 \times 8$ or $2 \times 8 \times 4$__. Record results in the table.

9. How do the volume and surface area appear to have changed?

   The volume has remained constant and the surface area has increased with each slide.

10. By counting, find the volume and surface area of this new rectangular solid and record them in the table.

    Answers will vary.

11. What can you conclude from this activity?

    Answers will vary, but possible responses include: I conclude that surface area can change even when the volume does not. A cube has the least amount of surface area for a given volume.

Proportional Thinking

1. If two ratios are equivalent you can form them into a proportion.

For example: $\frac{1}{3} = \frac{2}{6}$

Write at least three more proportions using ratios equivalent to $\frac{1}{3}$.

$\frac{1}{3} = \frac{3}{9}$ $\frac{1}{3} = \frac{4}{12}$ $\frac{1}{3} = \frac{5}{15}$

2. Write at least three proportions using the ratio $\frac{2}{5}$.

$\frac{2}{5} = \frac{4}{10}$ $\frac{2}{5} = \frac{8}{20}$ $\frac{2}{5} = \frac{6}{15}$

3. Write at least three proportions using the ratio $\frac{8}{7}$.

$\frac{8}{7} = \frac{\ }{\ }$ $\frac{8}{7} = \frac{\ }{\ }$ $\frac{8}{7} = \frac{\ }{\ }$

4. In the proportion $\frac{1}{2} = \frac{3}{6}$ the cross products are represented by 1×6 and 2×3.

Follow the process in this example to evaluate the cross products for each of your proportions in questions 1–3.

$1 \times 9 = 3 \times 3$ $1 \times 12 = 3 \times 4$ $1 \times 15 = 3 \times 5$
$9 = 9$ $12 = 12$ $15 = 15$

Examine and compare your cross products. What do you notice? *Answers will vary. One possible response is: You multiply the numerator on the left side by the denominator on the right side and you multiply the numerator on the right side by the denominator on the left side. The results of these two operations are equal.*

---

4. Another way to determine the amount of extra cardboard is to calculate the surface area of your cubical cereal box and compare it to the surface area of your original box.

a. Calculate the surface area of your cubical cereal box.
Answers will vary.

b. The surface area of your original cereal box was *Answers will vary.*

c. Find the difference in the surface areas of your original cereal box and your new cubical cereal box.
Answers will vary.

d. Using this method, the area of your extra cardboard is: *Answers will vary.*

5. You have calculated the amount of extra cardboard using two different methods. Are the results the same? Should they be? Explain.
Answers will vary. The results differ due to accuracy of construction technique and measuring process.

6. The cubical cereal box saves approximately _____ square centimeters of cardboard. Explain your reasoning.
Answers will vary depending on which estimate the student thinks is more accurate.

7. Cardboard comes from _____ trees. If you are saving cardboard, then you are saving _____ trees.

5. Discuss with your group how to use cross products to solve this proportion. Solve it.

$$\frac{3}{4} = \frac{x}{32}$$
$$3 \times 32 = 4x$$
$$96 = 4x$$
$$\frac{96}{4} = \frac{4x}{4}$$
$$24 = x$$

6. Use cross products to solve the following proportions:

a. $\frac{3}{15} = \frac{a}{25}$

$$3 \times 25 = 15a$$
$$75 = 15a$$
$$\frac{75}{15} = \frac{15a}{15}$$
$$5 = a$$

b. $\frac{7}{4} = \frac{35}{x}$

$$4 \times 35 = 7x$$
$$140 = 7x$$
$$\frac{140}{7} = \frac{7x}{7}$$
$$20 = x$$

c. $\frac{4}{n} = \frac{12}{15}$

$$4 \times 15 = 12n$$
$$60 = 12n$$
$$\frac{60}{12} = \frac{12n}{12}$$
$$5 = n$$

d. $\frac{2}{5} = \frac{p}{100}$

$$2 \times 100 = 5p$$
$$200 = 5p$$
$$\frac{200}{5} = \frac{5p}{5}$$
$$40 = p$$

7. Now write your own proportion problem and solve it using cross products.
Answers will vary.

Proportions, Products, and Percents

1. Percent is defined as part of 100. Convert these percents to ratios with a base of 100.

$$25\% = \frac{25}{100} \qquad 130\% = \frac{130}{100} \qquad x\% = \frac{x}{100}$$

2. Convert these ratios to percents.

$$\frac{18}{100} = 18\% \qquad \frac{2}{100} = 2\% \qquad \frac{p}{100} = p\%$$

3. Set up proportions, use cross products, and convert these ratios to percents.

$$\frac{9}{20} = \frac{p}{100} \qquad \frac{3}{8} = \frac{p}{100} \qquad \frac{8}{5} = \frac{p}{100}$$
$$20 \times p = 9 \times 100 \qquad 8 \times p = 3 \times 100 \qquad 5 \times p = 8 \times 100$$
$$20p = 900 \qquad 8p = 300 \qquad 5p = 100$$
$$\frac{20p}{20} = \frac{900}{20} \qquad \frac{8p}{8} = \frac{300}{8} \qquad \frac{5p}{5} = \frac{800}{5}$$
$$p = 45 \qquad p = 37.5 \qquad p = 160$$
$$\frac{9}{20} = 45\% \qquad \frac{3}{8} = 37.5\% \qquad \frac{8}{5} = 160\%$$

4. There are _____ students in class today. Find out how many would prefer raisin bran to shredded wheat for breakfast: _____
Use proportions to calculate the percent of students that prefers raisin bran.
Answers will vary.

5. If 780,000 tons of cardboard are used this year for packaging, and 187,200 tons of it are thrown away, what percent may be recycled?
One possible procedure follows:

$$780,000 - 187,200 = 592,800$$
$$\frac{592,800}{780,000} = \frac{p}{100}$$
$$780,000 \cdot p = 592,800 \cdot 100$$
$$780,000 \cdot p = 59,280,000$$
$$p = \frac{59,280,000}{780,000}$$
$$p = 76$$

76% may be recycled.

5. Fill in the table by collecting information from people in your group and in another group.

Student Name	Area of Leftover Cardboard (in cm)	Percent of Cardboard the Cubical Cereal Box Saves
1.	*Answers will vary.*	
2.		
3.		
4.		
5.		
6.		
7.		

6. Do cubical cereal boxes of different sizes save similar percents of cardboard? Explain.
Answers will vary.

Imagine That!

1. Your leftover cardboard equals _Answers will vary._ square centimeters.

2. Use a proportion and solve for p to find the percent your leftover cardboard represents of the cardboard required by the original cereal box. Round your solution to the nearest whole percent.

$$\frac{p}{100} = \frac{\text{Area of Leftover Cardboard}}{\text{Surface Area Original Box}}$$

Answers will vary.

3. A cubical cereal box would save _Answers will vary._ % of the cardboard used by the _Answers will vary._ company to package their cereal.

4. Is this a significant amount? Explain.
Answers will vary. The amount of cardboard saved depends primarily on the shape of the cereal box. The closer the dimensions are to that of a cube, the less cardboard saved. Most multiple serving cereal boxes are similar in shape and save approximately 20 percent of the cardboard. The single serving cereal boxes, however, more closely approximate a cube, and they save approximately 7 percent of the cardboard when transformed into a cube.

5. One face of a cubical cereal box is _____17_____ % of the cardboard needed to construct it. The rectangle you made with the leftover cardboard represents _Answers will vary._ % of the cardboard required to construct a cubical cereal box. What do you notice?

6. There are _Answers will vary._ students in your class. If your classmates' results are similar to yours, then approximately how many additional cubical cereal boxes could you construct using everyone's extra pieces? Explain this.

Imagine This!

1. How does the area of the rectangle made with your leftover cardboard compare visually with the total amount of cardboard used to make your cubical cereal box?
It appears to be about the same size as or greater than one face of the cube.

2. Percents provide another way to express this comparison. Set up a proportion to find the percent of leftover cardboard to the cardboard used to build your cubical cereal box. Round your solution to the nearest whole percent.
Answers will vary depending on shape of cereal box, but most likely will range between 15% and 30%.

3. A cubical cereal box has _____6_____ congruent faces. Therefore one face is what fractional part of the cube? $\frac{1}{6}$

4. Set up and solve a proportion to convert the above fractional part to the nearest whole percent.

$\frac{1}{6} = \frac{p}{100}$

$6p = 100$

$p = \frac{100}{6}$

$p = 16.67$

$\frac{1}{6} = 17\%$

5. Calculate the surface area and volume of a 4 × 4 × 4 unit cube. Record your results in the table.

a. Is there a pattern in how the surface area is changing? Explain.
The surface area increases by a factor of 4 (2^2) as you double the edge of the cube.

b. Is the volume changing in the same way? Explain.
The volume increases by a factor of 8 (2^3) as you double the edge of the cube.

6. Record the surface area and volume for an 8 × 8 × 8 unit cube.

Unit Cube Size	Surface Area in Square Units	Volume in Cubic Units
1 × 1 × 1	6	1
2 × 2 × 2	24	8
4 × 4 × 4	96	64
8 × 8 × 8	384	512

7. Based on these results, write a conclusion that describes what happens to the surface area and volume of a cube when you double the length of each side. *Answers will vary. Responses should be similar to those in 5.*

More or Less

1. What do you think will happen to the surface area and volume of a cube if you double its dimensions?
Answers will vary. Some students might predict that the surface area and/or the volume will also double.

2. Begin with a 1 × 1 × 1 unit cube. Record its surface area and volume in the table.

3. Double the length of each side to build a 2 × 2 × 2 unit cube. Determine the surface area and volume. Record your results in the table.

a. Did the surface area double? Explain.
No, it more than doubled. It went from 6 to 24 (or 1 to 4)! It quadrupled.

b. Did the volume double? Explain.
No, it more than doubled. It went from 1 to 8!

4. Double the length of each side again and build a 4 × 4 × 4 unit cube. Predict the

surface area: <u>*Answers will vary*</u> and the volume: <u>*Answers will vary*</u>

5. When you double the length of each edge of a cereal box it takes

_____4_____ times as much cardboard to construct it, and the cereal box

will hold _____8_____ times as much cereal! Explain how more is less.

Answers will vary. One possible response is: It takes four times more cardboard to make the "doubled" box, but it holds eight times more cereal. It would be like getting the cereal in eight regular boxes packaged in only four, saving the cardboard of four boxes!

6. If you are concerned about the environment and want to conserve our natural resources and reduce waste, does it matter which size cereal box you buy? Explain.

Both the shape and the size of the box are important in reducing waste in packaging. It takes less cardboard and, therefore, less trees to make a cubical box to hold a given amount of cereal. And it saves even more cardboard to make large cubical boxes.

More Is Less

1. Cereal can often be purchased in at least two different sizes—regular and large. For this activity, consider your cubical cereal box to be a regular-size cereal box. If you double the length of each edge of your regular-size cereal box to construct a large-size cereal box, predict how much cardboard you would need to build it. How much cereal will it hold?
Answers will vary. It will hold eight times as much cereal.

2. In the table below, record the data for your regular-size cereal box by referring to Student Sheets 1.3 and 2.1.

3. Determine and record the length for each edge of your large-size cereal box by doubling the edge length of your regular-size cereal box.

4. Calculate and record the surface area and volume for your large-size cubical cereal box.

Cubical Cereal Box	Length of Each Edge	Surface Area	Volume
Regular-size	*Answers will vary.*		
Large-size			